D0902009

Joseph Ben Meir Zabara

THE BOOK OF DELIGHT

R5
380.0810

THE BOOK OF DELIGHT

BY JOSEPH BEN MEIR ZABARA

TRANSLATED BY

MOSES HADAS

WITH AN INTRODUCTION BY

MERRIAM SHERWOOD

NEW YORK

COLUMBIA UNIVERSITY PRESS

DROPSIE COLLEGE
LIBRARY

Copyright © 1932 Columbia University Press, New York
Second printing and Columbia Paperback Edition 1960
Manufactured in the United States of America

This book was originally published as
Volume XVI of the series known as
Records of Civilization, Sources and Studies
and was edited under the auspices of the
Department of History, Columbia University

J. Q. R. - Columbia University Press - $1.50 - 12/11/60

PREFACE

The Book of Delight was first employed as a translation for *Sepher Shaashuim* by the late Israel Abrahams in his paper on Zabara. The excellent edition of the text by Professor Davidson (see page 42) is the basis of the present version. The translator has adopted Professor Davidson's division into chapters, and has also translated, with slight modifications, the rubrics which Professor Davidson provided. The Epistle Dedicatory is not an integral part of the book and has therefore been relegated to the end of the volume.

This translation, which is, to our knowledge, the only complete one in a European language with the exception of a Catalan version published during the year 1931 (see page 42), was made some four years ago. With a view to collaborating with the translator in providing an introduction, Mrs. Franklin Hollander and Dr. Sylvan Moolten (to whom the translator's best thanks are due) made some notes on the stories and the medical portions of the book respectively. Composite authorship proved impracticable, and Dr. Sherwood agreed to undertake the work, quite independently of what had been done. Any serious student of Zabara must refer to Dr. Davidson's learned introduction, particularly for his philological notes. The author of the present introduction has treated *The Book of Delight* from an angle especially appropriate for the series in which it appears, namely as a record of civilization. To the Editor of that series, Professor Austin P. Evans, the authors of both translation and introduction wish to express gratitude for his unfailing kindness and interest.

References in the footnotes are made by author only or by author and title. Fuller bibliographical information is to be found in the Bibliography (pages 187-98).

Columbia University
July, 1932

M. H. and M. S.

CONTENTS

DROPSIE COLLEGE LIBRARY

Great dread falleth upon Zabara when he heareth this matter, but he is assured of Enan that no harm will befall him.

CHAPTER XII 149

Wherein Zabara sojourneth in the city of Enan for a space of time. He considereth the folk thereof and findeth them wicked and sinful. The daughter of a certain wicked man of that town had found favor in the eyes of Enan and he was become enamored of her. Zabara reproveth Enan, setting forth that it beseemed him ill to wed the daughter of an unlettered man. Enan hearkeneth to Zabara's voice and taketh to wife another maiden, that was a learned man's daughter. In the course of their discussion of women and their qualities, Enan relateth the story of a certain washerwoman who caused dire commotion in the city and warfare so dread that 220 men were slain.

CHAPTER XIII 161

Wherein Zabara doth despise the men of that place, and desireth to return to his own land, to visit R. Sheshet Benveniste, in whose honor he did compose this book.

THE SEATS OF THE SOUL 167

EPISTLE DEDICATORY 179

BIBLIOGRAPHY 187

INDEX 199

INTRODUCTION

INTRODUCTION

(Works marked with an asterisk * have not been available to me for consultation.)

The object of the following study is to determine if possible to what extent the fifteen stories told by Zabara in his *Book of Delight* were known to the medieval Christian literature of Western Europe. This is not by any means, however, the only interesting literary problem offered by the work in question. There is much yet to be done in the investigation of oriental, and possibly of classical, sources for Zabara's tales.[1] To the student of the history of medicine, the various medical theories set forth, not only in *The Book of Delight* but also in Zabara's *Seats of the Soul*,[2] are of interest. The salient points of these theories have, in the present study, been outlined in their relation to the medical ideas of the author's time. *The Book of Delight* is, furthermore, liberally sprinkled with proverbs and anecdotes. These, too, offer a rich field for research; but, except in cases where, in the course of my principal investigation, I have happened upon sayings similar to Zabara's, I have not made a special study of the proverbs. In spite of the fact that a thorough exploration of all these avenues of research has been impossible, it is hoped that the contribution offered in the following pages may not be without value and interest.

After a brief account of Zabara's times and of what is known of his life, I shall be ready to present the results of

1 The oriental and the classical questions I can only with justice leave to those who are specialists in the two fields. Dr. Israel Davidson (pp. xxxviii-xlviii) indicates some of the oriental parallels; but the subject is worthy of a special study.

2 *The Treatise on Uroscopy* is sometimes given as Zabara's but is probably not by him (see Davidson, pp. xcvii-xcviii).

my hunt for parallels in the Christian narrative literature of Western Europe.[3]

Joseph ben Meïr ibn Zabara lived and wrote and practiced medicine in Barcelona in the latter half of the twelfth century. Both the time and the place are significant. Hebrew culture was at its height in Spain, and in no other region of Western Europe did the Jews find such widespread recognition of their abilities. From the Arab invasion of Spain at the beginning of the eighth century until the Almoravide conquest at the end of the eleventh, the Jews had enjoyed the favor of the Mohammedan rulers. They had proved themselves indispensable allies in the conquest and had been rewarded with signal marks of confidence by the conquerors. Cordova became the great center of Hebrew-Arabian culture in the West. With the coming of the Almoravides in 1086, the persecution of the Jews began and many of them left Spain. But it was not until the middle of the following century, when the fanatical Almohades fell upon Mohammedan Spain and incorporated it in their vast empire, that the persecution of the Jews became consistent and vigorous. At that time there was a general exodus of the oppressed race. The majority of the Jews fled across the border into the Christian kingdoms of the North: Castile, Leon, Aragon, and to a lesser extent Catalonia, welcomed the fugitives.

The same qualities that had won them the favor of their Arab patrons in the past now gave them a similar standing with the Christian princes who were engaged in the reconquest of Spain from the Mohammedans. The Jews not only helped materially to finance these campaigns, but also were frequently appointed to important offices; such as that of governor of a fortress, envoy, and especially tax-collector, their knowledge of finance fitting them particularly for the latter post. Their reputation for learning and, above all, their skill in medicine and other sciences, brought them into close personal contact with the upper classes, even to the extent of inter-

[3] Almost none of the Christian parallels that I have found are earlier than Zabara, whose sources would seem to have been oriental.

marriage with some of the noble families; while many a king of Leon or of Castile at this period had a Jewish scholar for his intimate adviser, and this notwithstanding protests from Rome. In general, the political and economic status of the Jews in northern Spain did not differ sensibly from that of their Christian compatriots; frequently it included special privileges.[4]

The latter half of the twelfth century, therefore, has a peculiar significance in the history of the Spanish Jews. Forced to abandon the South, with its intellectual center at Cordova, they carried that culture which they had built up under Arab encouragement, into the Christian North. Their intellectual acquisitions, instead of being lost through dispersion, continued to flourish in full force through another half century at least after the coming of the Almohades. What has been called the Golden Age of Hebrew culture in Spain is generally considered to have included the period from the end of the tenth century to the first part of the thirteenth. The contributions of Joseph Zabara to that culture fall, therefore, within the last portion of the Golden Age.

For the student of medieval literature, the Jewish writers of that time have a twofold importance: In the first place, their works are interesting in themselves; in the second — and this is of even wider significance for general cultural history — one of the main avenues by which the learning and literature of the East and of ancient Greece reached western Europe, was the Jews.[5] Just as it is impossible to think of medieval commerce without the Jew as financier and banker, so one cannot conceive of what medieval literature, science or philosophy would have become without the Jews as intermediaries. It will certainly never be known how many scientific works of Arabic or Greek origin, or how many tales out

[4] Jacobs, in his article, "Spain," in the *Jewish Encyclopedia,* XI, 484-502, gives an excellent account, with references to sources, of the status of the Jews in Spain during the Middle Ages. See also Graetz (III, IV), Amador de los Ríos, Keyserling, Regné, Dozy, Krauskopf; and cf. Haskins (Chap. IX).

[5] Cf., among others, Bédier, p. 83; Lancereau, p. xxiii; Montaiglon et Raynaud, I, xxvii.

of the story-telling East, found their way into Europe by means of Hebrew or through translations, made by Jews, into Latin or the vernacular. Many of the Jewish translators or interpreters who performed this service are bound to be forever nameless, not only because the Middle Ages was careless about authorship, but also because it was not uncommon for a Christian writer to employ a Jew to translate a work to which the employer's name would be given.[6]

The Jews were adapted by the circumstances of their life to the work of translation. They were at least bilingual, for they must know Hebrew as well as the vernacular of the country in which they had settled. Any work, therefore, which had been translated into Hebrew had the chance of an enormous circulation among the Jews in all the Western European lands and might easily find its way thence into the various literatures of Europe.[7] Spain, with its Arab population, formed a natural door for the entrance of oriental works into Europe. An outstanding example of the Jew as intermediary between the literatures of the East and the West is Petrus Alphonsus of Spain, the twelfth-century Jewish convert to Christianity, whose *Disciplina clericalis*, a collection of Arabic tales done into Latin, formed a rich source for story-tellers in other European countries. His work was translated into French as early as the twelfth century, and there are later medieval versions in Gascon, Spanish, Italian, German, English and Icelandic;[8] while the *Gesta Romanorum* and other *exempla* collections, as well as the *Fabliaux*, used it freely as a source.

Perhaps the most striking contribution of the Jews of the Middle Ages to Western-European culture was their share in the transmission of Arabian medicine and philosophy to the occidental world. All the Jews acquainted with Arabic were not, of course, in Spain; but even before the persecution instituted by the Almohades, the conquest of Toledo by Al-

6 See Steinschneider, *Hebraeische Uebersetzungen*, pp. 971 ff.

7 Cf. Landau, p. xiii.

8 See Hilka und Söderhjelm, pp. xii-xv, for an account of these translations.

fonso VI of Castile in 1085 gave an impetus to the translation of Moorish medical works, and this labor was performed to a large extent by Jews. Moreover, medicine seems to have had a very special attraction for the medieval Jews. They had flourishing schools for the study of that science at Arles and at Narbonne, and they are believed by many scholars to have been largely responsible for the founding of the medical school at Montpellier, first mentioned in 1137.[9] The introduction of Arabian medicine, which held sway in Europe for several centuries, was thus to a very great extent the work of the Jews.

Joseph Zabara was one among many writers who gave the period at whose close he lived its brilliance in the history of Jewish culture. His name is not among the most famous of his time; the only known reference to him by a contemporary is the mention of "the scholar Zabara" by Joseph Kimhi, of Narbonne.[10] Nevertheless, Zabara is quite representative of that culture to which so many names of greater note belong. For one thing, the fact that a practicing physican in a great city should not only have written on medical subjects but should also have proved his undoubted talent in the field of pure literature, is quite in the spirit of his contemporaries.[11]

The great period of Jewish culture in Spain may be said to have begun with the founding of the Talmudic academy at Cordova by Hasdai ibn Shaprut (*c.* 915-*c.* 980), a physician and scholar, confidential minister to the Calif Abd ar-Rahman

[9] See Rashdall, II, 115 ff.

[10] In regard to Joseph Kimhi, see below, p. 8. Kimhi twice mentions Zabara in his commentary on *Proverbs* (cf. Davidson, p. xxiv).

[11] For the following section dealing with Hebrew literature of the Golden Age, I am largely indebted to Dr. Hadas, the present translator of Zabara, for the use of his notes and bibliography. A few references may be given: Karpeles, I, 291-477, gives a useful outline of the literature; Abrahams, *A Short History of Jewish Literature*, is very brief and lacks thoroughness. The best work on the subject is that of Winter und Wünsche, with selections in German translation prefaced by biographical notes. The various articles in the *Jewish Encyclopedia* and in the *Encyclopædia Judaica* are perhaps the best resource for the general student. Delitzsch may also be mentioned, and a good handbook for the medieval period is that of Oesterley and Box, Part IV, pp. 209-90. See also Bebel.

III and to the latter's son and successor Al Hakim. Samuel ibn Nagdela (993-1055), a product of the academy, was vizier to King Habus, but further distinguished himself as grammarian, Talmudist and poet. Nagdela was patron of one of the greatest poets of the age, Solomon ibn Gabirol (*c.* 1020-*c.* 1058),[12] whose *Fons vitae* — for Gabirol was a philosopher as well as a poet — attributed in a corrupt form to "Avicembron," exercised a great influence on the Christians in the field of scholastic philosophy. There were writers such as Judah Halevi (1086?-1140?),[13] another great poet and a philosopher as well; Bahya ibn Paquda, who lived during the first half of the eleventh century and whose *Hobhoth ha-Lebhabhoth*, or *Duties of the Heart*,[14] won a high reputation; and Isaac Alfasi (1013-1103), who abstracted the legal portions from the mass of Talmudic literature.

To the Golden Age belong three famous families of scholars and writers: the Kimhis, the Ibn Ezras and the Ibn Tibbons. The three learned members of the first, Joseph (*c.* 1105-*c.* 1170), Moses (*c.* 1190), and David (1160-1235), were all biblical exegetes. David, more particularly, exerted an influence upon Christian exegesis. Moses ibn Ezra (*c.* 1070-1138?) was a poet with a reputation almost equal to that of Ibn Gabirol and Judah Halevi; while the works of Abraham ibn Ezra (1093-1167?) include poetry, philosophical and mathematical works, and biblical commentaries. The Ibn Tibbons were prodigiously industrious members of the large

12 See Wise, in the *Jewish Encyclopedia*, VI, 526-32; Munk; Husik, Chap. V, pp. 59-79.

13 Translations of selections from both Ibn Gabirol and Judah Halevi are available in the "Schiff Library of Jewish Classics:" *Selected Religious Poems of Solomon ibn Gabirol*, translated into English verse by Israel Zangwill from a critical text edited by Israel Davidson; and *Selected Poems of Judah Halevi*, translated into English by Nina Salaman, chiefly from the critical text edited by Heinrich Brody. Judah Halevi's philosophical work, the *Khozari*, has been translated into English by H. Hirschfeld; new edition with preface by M. M. Kaplan.

14 First part translated into English by Hyamson.

body of Jewish translators mentioned above.[15] Most of their translations were from Arabic into Hebrew.[16]

Above the rest towers the figure of Moses Maimonides (1135-1204), an almost exact contemporary of Zabara. Forced by the tyranny of the Almohades to leave Cordova, Maimonides settled in Cairo, where he became chief rabbi and also physician at the court of Saladin. Besides his widely-known *Moreh Nebukhim* or *Guide to the Perplexed*,[17] he compiled the *Mishneh Torah* or *Deuteronomy*, a codification of the immense body of Talmudic law, and wrote several medical treatises also. His works not only brought about a century-long religious controversy among the Jews, but greatly influenced, as well, the Christians who dealt with scholastic philosophy.

Another writer of the period, the poet Judah al-Harizi (*c.* 1170-*c.* 1230), a younger contemporary of Zabara, bears a certain resemblance to the latter, not only in the fact that his *Tahkemoni* and his translation of the *Maqamat*, or *Assemblies* (*Séances*) of the Arab Al-Hariri,[18] are similar in form to Zabara's *Book of Delight*, but also in the circumstance of his being, like Zabara, a physician. He translated into Hebrew Maimonides' *Guide to the Perplexed*, composed by the author in Arabic, and also a gynecological treatise of Sheshet Benveniste, Zabara's patron.

A work of a very different sort is the *Masaot* or *Itineraries* [19] of the twelfth-century traveler, Benjamin of Tudela, whose exact description of his journey through Southern Europe, Western Asia and Northern Africa, is a valuable historical source.

Joseph Zabara, then, was heir to a long and noble tradition

15 Pages 5-7.

16 For Hebrew translations and translators see the article "Translations," by Broydé, in the *Jewish Encyclopedia*, XII, 219-29; also, Steinschneider, *Hebraeische Uebersetzungen*; and Haskins, Chap. IX.

17 English translation by Friedländer.

18 See especially the excellent translation and introduction by Chenery.

19 A good English translation has been made by Grünhut and Adler; there are several others.

of intellectual activity. Like those who had preceded him and like his learned contemporaries, he interested himself in various fields of knowledge. He does not stand out as an innovator, as the more detailed study of his works, presented below, will show; but he was well grounded in the intellectual acquisitions of his time, in medicine especially, but also, one would judge, in astronomy, in physics, and in philosophy. He cites with great frequency the Bible, the Talmudic writings, the Greek philosophers. These citations, sometimes in the form of anecdotes, do not prove a first-hand acquaintance with the lives and writings of the personages mentioned. Many of them, especially those referring to the Greeks, were the stock in trade of medieval writers, Christian as well as Jewish; although a given anecdote or saying will be told now of one, now of another philosopher. Yet, whether or not at first hand, the physician of Barcelona shows himself familiar in certain instances with particular statements of a given "sage" of antiquity.[20] Zabara also had an extensive acquaintance with literature. This is shown not only by the excellence of his style in both prose and poetry, but also by the fact that most of the tales that he tells have parallels elsewhere, parallels which cannot be traced to him as source. He was, in short, a more than ordinarily cultured man, whose name finds an appropriate place at the end of the Golden Age of Hebrew culture in Spain.

Nearly nothing is known with certainty of Zabara's life, and that little must be deduced almost entirely from his works. In *The Book of Delight*, which is ostensibly autobiographical, the author states that he is a physician of Barcelona and the son of a physician.[21] These statements may doubtless be accepted as true, all the more since medical questions preoccupy him largely in *The Book of Delight* and since his other

[20] For example, Zabara's remark about the buoyancy of salt water as evidenced in the Dead Sea (see below, p. 132), Dr. Davidson (p. lxxix) places side by side a similar passage from Aristotle's *Meteorologica* (Book II, Chap. III) and another from Rabbi Gershon; Zabara is not necessarily citing Aristotle directly. Cf. note 114, below.

[21] See pp. 47, 145.

extant work, *The Seats of the Soul*, deals with medical subjects. He dedicates *The Book of Delight* to Sheshet Benveniste of Barcelona, speaking of him as his "lost lord." This qualification of his fellow townsman, together with somewhat vague references to an enemy and to exile, in the same dedication and again at the end of the work,[22] have been taken by some scholars as indicating that the frame of *The Book of Delight* is autobiographical and not a mere fiction; in other words, that Zabara was lured away from his native city by someone who proved to be his enemy, but that he was at last able to return home.[23] However, the device of inventing a framework in which to place disconnected stories, dialogues and moral or scientific instruction was so common in the Middle Ages, that corroboration from some other source is certainly necessary before one accepts such a frame as a record of fact. The date of Zabara's birth is generally accepted as *c.* 1140.[24]

The Book of Delight is Zabara's most important work. It is a framework narrative; its disparate contents — short tales, scientific discussions and proverbs — are given an artificial unity by being placed in the mouths of the characters of a larger story created for the express purpose of imparting to the reader the short tales, the scientific discussions and the proverbs. This is a simple device, which has been resorted to by story-tellers from ancient times down to the modern age, and one with which many illustrious names are connected. Chaucer is doubtless the first such that would occur to English readers.

The frame containing the shorter stories may be of varying importance: sometimes, as in *The Golden Ass* of Apuleius, the stories are merely incidental; more often it is the frame that has been imagined as an excuse for telling the stories. The

[22] Pages 164-65, 177-81.

[23] See Davidson, pp. xxiii-xxviii; Abrahams, in the *Jewish Quarterly Review*, VI, pp. 502-32, especially 503-5. Cf. Abrahams, *The Book of Delight and Other Papers*, pp. 9-61.

[24] See Davidson, Appendix A, cv-cxi, where he outlines the reasoning by which he arrives at this date.

latter is apparently the case in *The Book of Delight.* In its conception *The Book of Delight* proves, upon analysis, to be a more ambitious undertaking than the usual framework narrative; it is not, like *The Thousand and One Nights*, the *Decameron*, or *The Canterbury Tales*, a collection of stories merely. In it the author attempts to set forth, frequently by the common medieval device of questions and answers, the sum of his knowledge and of his beliefs, literary, moral and scientific. The large amount of space devoted to the last is to be explained by his profession, that of physician. But the moral tales which he tells form an important part of the work; they are the most interesting part for us because of the relation they bear to the narrative writings of his contemporaries in other lands. Zabara's scientific, especially his medical, knowledge is essentially that which was traditional in his time among the Arabs and which was spreading throughout Europe as Christians, whether through commerce or crusades or through the Jew as middleman, became more and more intimately acquainted with Mohammedan culture. But the stories in *The Book of Delight* arrest our attention more particularly because, while some of them are tales that were the common property of East and West in the Middle Ages, others seem not to have been generally known, perhaps not known at all, to the Christian literature of Western Europe. These were not known, at least in the form in which Zabara recounts them. The themes are, for the most part, common enough — for example, several of them deal with the faithlessness of woman — but the tales themselves apparently have no parallels in the Christian West.

The Book of Delight contains fifteen stories, exclusive of mere anecdotes recording some alleged witty saying of a sage of antiquity, Socrates, Diogenes and Aristotle being the favorites. These fifteen stories belong to the class of apologues or *exempla*; that is, they are intended to point a moral. To facilitate the discussion, the stories are numbered below and their place in the present translation of *The Book of Delight* indicated:

1. The fox and the leopard (pages 55-70). This story is itself the framework for the five immediately following:
2. The fox and the lion (pages 58-59)
3. The silversmith of Babylonia (pages 59-61)
4. The woodcutter of Damascus (page 61)
5. The faithful husband and the faithless wife (pages 61-66)
6. The Roman knight and the widow (pages 67-69)
7. The clever peasant girl (pages 71-76)
8. The dishonest precentor (pages 80-82)
9. Jacob of Cordova and the nobleman (pages 83-85)
10. The true and the false son (pages 85-88)
11. The story of Tobit (pages 90-95)
12. The miracle of the paralytic (pages 95-98)
13. The princess and the winter-blooming flowers (pages 122-23)
14. The fox in the garden (pages 124-25)
15. The washerwoman and the demon (pages 156-60)

These stories fall into three categories as regards the aim of the present essay:[25] certain of them — for example, The Roman knight and the widow, and The fox in the vineyard — are so familiar even today that it has not been necessary to do more than suggest a few of the well-known versions; others, such as The old woman and the demon and The true and the false son, were widely known in former times but are so no longer; still others have, as far as I have yet discovered, no Western Christian parallels, although in some cases this or that feature of the tale occurs elsewhere, and although, as mentioned above,[26] the themes were common ones in the Middle Ages.

The richest field for occidental parallels to these moral stories of Zabara, which are exactly similar in purpose to the

[25] See pp. 3-4. In the following discussion I have rarely referred to folklore analogies to the stories, but have in almost all cases confined my study to medieval literary texts.

[26] Page 12.

exempla of the Christian preachers, I have found to be precisely the *exempla* collections of the Middle Ages. Writers like Walter Map, Boccaccio, Der Stricker in his lighter moments, the composers of the *fabliaux*, offer scarcely a parallel, except in the case of some particularly widespread tale. Zabara's stories were for moral instruction, rather than for amusement. His was a book of spiritual, not sensuous, delight, in somewhat the same sense as was the *Hortus deliciarum* of the pedagogically-minded German contemporary of Zabara, the Abbess Herrad of Hohenburg.

I shall discuss, to begin with, those stories of Zabara to which I have found medieval Christian parallels. The well-known story of the Matron of Ephesus is the first of these. This is here told as a warning against the treachery of wives. It would be superfluous to discuss in the present study all the ramifications of this widespread story, which has engaged the attention of so many scholars.[27] It found its way with equal fitness into the *exempla* collection of the preachers, the works of writers for the aristocracy, and the repertory of the *jongleurs* of the market place and tavern. According to one's point of view, it may be edifying or entertaining, the latter if one's sense of humor is of the robust sort. The different versions of the story vary considerably in revolting detail. Zabara's rendering leaves out none of the gruesomeness. On the other hand, John of Salisbury,[28] who based his account on that of Petronius Arbiter,[29] has a comparatively mild version. Here the knight who guards the corpse is obliged to exert considerable persuasion, even stratagem, to win the widow to his advances. Although it is the widow who proposes to replace the stolen corpse by that of her husband, she makes the proposal only after the knight has threatened to stab himself. There is no mutilation of the husband's corpse, and there is no subsequent marriage of the two partners in guilt.

In Zabara's version, there are no extenuating circumstances

27 See, among others, Dunlop-Liebrecht, pp. 40-41, 464; Grisebach.
28 Lib. viii, cap. 11 (ed. Webb, II, 753b-755a).
29 Cap. 111-12.

as far as the widow is concerned. It is she who solicits the favors of the guard, and she insists, notwithstanding her lover's protests, upon digging up her husband's corpse. The widow herself mutilates the corpse to make it resemble that of the hanged man, and after it is all over she marries the guard. In several of the versions, the guard, filled with horror at the widow's actions, refuses to marry her even though he had previously promised to do so.[30]

In the *fabliau* usually entitled *La Femme au tombeau*,[31] the story has been materially altered to give it the character of levity peculiar to these jovial tales. The scene is transferred from the usual Rome or Ephesus to the more familiar Flanders. There is no hanged criminal to be guarded and consequently the substitution of the husband's body for the corpse on the gibbet does not take place. The seduction of the widow here is merely the result of a wager between a passing knight and his squire.

In Zabara's version, as in that of the *Seven Wise Masters,* the action passes in Rome. In others, for example, in the *Satyricon*, it is placed in Ephesus.

The seventh tale in *The Book of Delight*, The clever peasant girl, has many variants, a number of which belong to the realm of folklore.[32] The two outstanding characteristics of this story are: (1) seemingly nonsensical remarks that prove to have had a meaning, and (2) a clever maiden, usually a peasant girl, who interprets correctly the signification of these remarks. In Zabara's story an oriental monarch dreams of an ape that jumps on the neck of his wives and his concubines. One of his eunuchs goes to fetch a sage who can interpret the dream. On the way he meets a peasant and makes a series of apparently foolish remarks to him. He stays the night at the

30 For example, the versions contained in the following: *The Seven Wise Masters* (published by Ellis, III, 71-78); *Le cento novelle antiche*, no. 59.

31 Montaiglon et Raynaud, III, no. 70.

32 For the bibliography of this folklore motif, in both western and oriental literature, see Köhler, II, 602 f.; Wesselski, *Märchen des Mittelalters*, p. 197; Benfey,* "Die kluge Dirne," in his *Kleinere Schriften*, II, 156-223; Bolte und Polivka (annotations to the Brothers Grimm, "Die kluge Bauerntochter," in their *Kinder- und Hausmärchen*, no. 94), II, 348-73; Frazer, II, 564 f.

peasant's house. A daughter of the latter correctly interprets the remarks, is taken to the king, and tells him that the ape of his dream is a man in disguise in the harem. This being found true, the wives, the concubines, and the man are put to death and the clever girl marries the king, who vows to be monogamous thenceforth.

The same story occurs in the thirteenth-century *Compilatio singularis exemplorum.*[33] Here, however, the Queen of Sheba is brought into the story. The king who dreams of the ape is the King of Sheba. Apparently he has but one wife. The eunuch of Zabara's version is here a knight, and the clever girl is a noble maiden already known to the knight. As he is on his way to fetch her to interpret the king's dream, he meets her bridegroom proceeding to the wedding. It is the bridegroom to whom the apparently foolish observations are made, and these are interpreted by the girl at the feast preceding the wedding. The girl, leaving her betrothed, goes to the king and by a ruse discovers the man among the queen's handmaidens. The queen and her lover are convicted and the clever girl marries the king. She is no other than the Queen of Sheba of biblical fame.

Some of the riddles solved by the clever girl in the above two versions are the same; others are different. The similar ones are: (1) Carry thou me and I will carry thee; (2) Has the grain standing in the field been harvested yet? (3) Is the corpse quite dead? The propounding of riddles was a favorite literary device of the Middle Ages, and some of those occurring in the above story are found elsewhere in quite a different setting.[34] For example, in the *Gesta Romanorum*[35] there is the story of a knight who makes a pact with the emperor's daughter to come back after seven years and marry her; if he fails her, she will be free to marry someone else. As the seventh year ends, the knight meets a king on his way to

[33] Translated into German by Wesselski (*Märchen des Mittelalters*, no. 7) from the *Compilatio singularis exemplorum** (pp. 4 f., ed. Hilka).

[34] For a bibliography of the riddle literature, see Wesselski, *Märchen des Mittelalters*, p. 197; Köhler, I, 197, II, 607 ff.

[35] No. 193 (ed. Oesterley); translated by Wesselski, *Mönchslatein*, no. CXVII.

wed the princess. The knight makes seemingly foolish observations to the king. Here it is the emperor who interprets them. Two of these remarks are similar to two which occur, not in Zabara's story, but in the *exemplum*, from the *Compilatio singularis exemplorum*, outlined above: (1) The bridge used where there is no bridge, and (2) Going to look for something (a net in the *Gesta Romanorum* and a doe in the *Compilatio*) left in a certain place a number of years previously.

John Gower [36] (fourteenth century) tells a story of a girl of fourteen, a knight's daughter, so clever that she not only satisfactorily solves the riddles whose solution is the price of her father's head, but very astutely tricks the king into marrying her. The story is not the same as that told by Zabara, but it has some similar features: the ability of a young girl to solve riddles, and her winning of a royal husband through this form of cleverness.

The ninth story, that of the merchant Jacob of Cordova and the nobleman who tried to rob him of a precious chain, is apparently not so widespread in the literature of the West as are some of the others. There is, however, a parallel to it in the thirteenth-century *Mensa philosophica*.[37] The external details are quite different in the latter from those in *The Book of Delight*, but the two stories undoubtedly go back ultimately to a common original. This is presumably oriental, for Davidson [38] mentions several Hebrew parallels and Wesselski [39] cites a similar story in Steele, *Kusa Jatakaya* (1871), page 256. According to Zabara, a Jewish merchant, Jacob of Cordova, acting as agent for the sale of a precious chain, permits a nobleman who is a favorite of the king to have the article taken into the nobleman's house for his wife's inspection. When Jacob applies to the nobleman for the return of the chain, the latter professes ignorance of the transaction and

[36] Book I (pp. 90-95, ed. Morley).

[37] Translated into German by Wesselski (*Mönchslatein*, no. CLI) from the *Mensa philosophica*,* 4, 12, p. 217.

[38] Page lxi.

[39] *Mönchslatein*, p. 254.

the merchant is unable to recover it. He complains to the judge, who thereupon calls a conclave of all the important men of the city. The nobleman in question comes with the rest and, after the oriental fashion, leaves his shoes at the door; whereupon, under the judge's orders, a servant, taking the nobleman's shoe as a token, goes to the wife of the latter and obtains the chain, which is duly returned to the merchant.

In the *Mensa philosophica* the oriental dress of the story is done away with. Here the king is "Philip" and the scene is laid in Paris. A merchant gives a bag of gold and silver to a burgher, an intimate of the king, for safe-keeping, and when the merchant asks for the return of his property, the burgher behaves in the same manner as the nobleman in Zabara's story. It is the king here who restores the bag of gold to its rightful owner. The incident of the shoe — a distinctively oriental trait — is necessarily altered. Philip asks the burgher for a ring which the latter has often begged him to accept. With this as a token, the money is obtained from the burgher's wife. The burgher is properly punished. All the differences in this story are clearly mere alterations in superficial detail, made for the purpose of adapting the tale to a western environment; that is, if the story was originally oriental. If the source is western, the changes were made for the same reason but in the inverse direction.

Davidson [40] cites as similar to Zabara's story: Number 118 in the *Gesta Romanorum*; Number 13 (should be 15) in the *Disciplina clericalis* of Petrus Alphonsus; Number 74 in the *Cento novelle antiche*; and Day 8, Number 10, in the *Decameron.* His reference appears to be wrong for the *Cento novelle antiche*: I find no similar story in that work. The *Disciplina clericalis* and the *Gesta Romanorum* tell the well-known apologue of the coffers of money left with a citizen, for safekeeping, by a traveler, and restored to the owner upon the refusal of the citizen to return them, through a quite different ruse suggested by an old woman. The only resemblance be-

40 Page lxi. In Winter und Wünsche, III, 150, a similar story told of Rudolph of Hapsburg is mentioned, but no reference for this story is given.

tween this story and that told by Zabara is the fact that property wrongfully retained by a person to whose care it has been confided is restored to its owner by a ruse. The coffer tale bears a slightly closer similarity to that of the *Mensa philosophica* than to Zabara's version, in that in the former it is a question of money entrusted to another for safe-keeping, not of a precious article loaned to a prospective buyer. Still further from Zabara's story is that told by Boccaccio: here a merchant recovers, by a ruse of his own inventing, money loaned to his mistress.

The tenth story is the very widespread one of the test by which the true son of a deceased man is distinguished from another, or others, claiming, for the sake of the inheritance, to have been his sons. Zabara's version differs in several particulars from those I have studied in the Western-European literature. In the latter the main points of the tale are as follows: A woman has two or more sons, only one of them being legitimate. Her husband dies knowing this, but unable to discover which is his son; yet he expresses the wish that his own son alone inherit the property. The father's corpse, by order of the person left in charge of the case by the father, is removed from the coffin, and it is stated that he who can inflict the deepest wound upon it in a single trial shall receive the inheritance. The true son alone refuses so to desecrate the corpse. He is thereupon recognized as the rightful heir. In the Old French *Jugement de Salemon* [41] and in the *De naturis rerum* of Alexander Neckam (twelfth century),[42] the weapon used to wound the father's corpse is a lance. There are three sons of the mother in the latter, while the former mentions but two. Étienne de Bourbon [43] (thirteenth century) and John of Bromyard [44] (end of the fourteenth century) mention three sons, but the wounding of the father's corpse is done with an arrow.

41 Published by Barbazan et Méon, II, 440-42.

42 Cap. CLXXVI (ed. Wright).

43 Ed. Lecoy de la Marche, no. 160.

44 *Summa prædicantium,** tit. *Filiatio* (this story published by Wright [*Latin Stories*, no. XXI] and translated by Wesselski, *Mönchslatein*, no. VI).

The *Gesta Romanorum*[45] tells of three illegitimate sons and one legitimate. The weapon used in the test, in this version also, is an arrow.

Thomas Wright[46] sees some resemblance to this story in that of Philip and Robert Falconbridge in Shakespeare's *King John*,[47] and also in the *Cento novelle antiche*;[48] but the similarity seems to me in both cases too slight to be significant.

In Zabara's version there are, as above stated, certain deviations from the story as presented in the western versions I have outlined: (1) The rival claimants to the inheritance are, in *The Book of Delight*, a merchant's legitimate son and the son of a female slave,[49] who has been treated by the merchant as a son during the absence of his own son on business. The true son comes back in dire straits after several years, to find his father dead and the slave regarded as the rightful heir to the property. The slave accuses the son of being an imposter. (2) The judge, to whom the two appeal, orders the bones of the deceased to be burned because of the latter's negligence in failing to leave a will. The slave consents, while the true son, rather than desecrate his father's grave, offers to abandon the inheritance to the slave. The property is thereupon awarded to its rightful owner and the other becomes his slave.

It is clear that this story is essentially the same as that of the *Jugement de Salemon* and related versions. Its chief divergencies are merely matters of detail reflecting oriental society and incompatible with European customs.[50]

The eleventh tale is the story of Tobit, well-known from the *Apocrypha*. Zabara's narration differs materially from the

45 No. 45 (ed. Oesterley). Dunlop-Liebrecht (p. 415) note that Thomas-Simon Gueulette (1683-1766) follows this version in his *Mille et un quart d'heure, Contes tartares*.

46 Page 218.

47 Act I, sc. 1.

48 No. 51.

49 It is not stated whether the latter is the man's son or not.

50 I might mention that the Talmudic version of the story gives a variation of the test of legitimacy: the rival heirs are ordered to knock on the father's grave and to ask him to state which is his true son. Clouston (I, 14) cites this version at length; and, after Clouston, Wesselski (*Mönchlatein*, pp. 200-1) gives it.

Apocryphal one; and there seems to be no other known version that has these differences. The story is not improved in Zabara's rendering of it; in fact, the plot is more loosely constructed than in the usual version, and some of the incidents are pointless. Zabara's version is without doubt a later, corrupted form of the legend, for it has lost certain reminiscences of mythology or folklore that are retained by the biblical story and those which follow the latter. The most striking deviations in *The Book of Delight* are the following: (1) The gallows incident, in which a miracle saves Tobias, the father, from hanging, occurs in Zabara's version alone. (2) Elijah, and not Raphael, is Tobit's guide in Zabara. (3) The demon persecuting Sara is not mentioned by name in *The Book of Delight*, and the only connection of the guide with the defeat of the demon is the fact that he tells Tobias's son that the liver of the fish will expel demons. He holds no personal encounter with Sara's persecutor. (4) The betrothal of Tobit [51] and Sara is, in Zabara's version, in no way related to the recovery of the money loaned by Tobit's father.

In one particular Zabara follows the Hebrew and the Aramaic texts of *Tobit* as against the Greek: the dog which accompanies Tobit in the latter is omitted from the other versions, as it is from that of Zabara.[52]

[51] Tobit is not mentioned by name in Zabara's account.

[52] The omission of the dog in the Hebrew texts is due to the fact that that animal was despised by the Hebrews. Its presence in the Greek text has been put forward as one of the evidences that the story has an Iranian background; for Raphael, according to this view, takes the place of Sraosha, and the dog is the companion of Sraosha in the Persian mythology. See, on the Iranian question: Stock, "Tobit, the Book of," in the *Encyclopædia Britannica* (11th ed.), XXVI, 1041-42; Breen, "Asmodeus," in the *Catholic Encyclopedia*, I, 792; Drum, "Tobias" (Part II), in *ibid.*, XIV, 750-53; Driscoll, "Raphael," in *ibid.*, XII, 640; Ginzberg, "Asmodeus," in the *Jewish Encyclopedia*, II, 217-20; Blau, "Raphael," in *ibid.*, X, 317-19; Mangenot, "Démon dans la Bible et la théologie juive," in Vacant et Mangenot, IV, cols. 322-39; Vacant, "Ange," in *ibid.*, I, cols. 1189-1271; Van den Gheyn, "Asmodée," in Vigouroux, I, cols. 1103-4; Gutmann, "Aschmedai," in the *Encyclopædia Judaica*, III, cols. 498-501. I am not attempting to discuss those questions relating to oriental religion, for that is outside the scope of the present study. The above references are given merely because of the particularly far-reaching interest which attaches to *The Story of Tobit*. The articles just cited contain further bibliographical material. That Zabara should

Perhaps the most interesting of the above-mentioned differences between Zabara's text and that of the *Apocrypha* is the substitution of Elijah for Raphael. In the *Book of Tobit* and in the later legends regarding Asmodeus, notably the *Testament of Solomon*,[53] Raphael is represented as the angel specially appointed to frustrate the demon Asmodeus, whose particular function it is to harass newly-married couples.[54] The substitution of Elijah may perhaps be explained by the fact that in the popular legends of the Jews he became more and more the recognized helper of those in distress, and — what touches the Tobit story more particularly — the preserver of marital happiness.[55]

The origin of Asmodeus is in dispute; some scholars derive his name from the Persian, others from the Hebrew. Thus it has been taken variously to mean "the destroyer," "the jealous," and "the incontinent." [56] But, as I have before stated, it is not my object here to trace the oriental background of the tales told by Zabara.

In general also, I am not considering in the present study the relations of folklore to these stories. However, in the case of Tobit a very alluring line of investigation may be indicated. Liljeblat [57] has pointed out, by a wealth of examples drawn from Western-European countries, the very striking similarity

include the story of Tabit is not strange. Jewish scholars did not become familiar with the Apocrypha until Azariah dei Rossi (*c.* 1514-78) pointed out its significance.

53 See Conybeare, in the *Jewish Quarterly Review*, XI, 1-45. The articles on Asmodeus, cited in the preceding note, summarize the results of research regarding this demon.

54 Cf. Conybeare, in the *Jewish Quarterly Review*, XI, 20-21. See further, Welter, L'Exemplum, no. 162, where the various matrimonial irregularities laying married couples open to the persecution of Asmodeus are listed by the anonymous author of the *exempla* collection there edited.

55 See Katten, "Elijahu," in the *Encyclopædia Judaica*, VI, cols. 485-94.

56 See references given in note 52 above. Cf. also *Sainte Bible de Vence*, VIII, 262 ("Dissertation sur les démons," pp. 260-66).

57 *Die Tobiasgeschichte und andere Märchen mit toten Helfern.* Cf. also Simrock. Wesselski (*Märchen des Mittelalters*, pp. 200-2) gives a useful bibliography covering the various folklore motifs in the Tobit story: among others, he mentions Plath,* in *Theologische Studien und Kritiken*, LXXIV (1901), pp. 377 f.; Schmidt, pp. 162-68; Bolte und Polivka, III, 490-517; Gunkel, pp. 73-74, 90-93.

between the story of Tobit and Sara, and the "demon-bride" tales current in those countries. The tales appear in an amazing variety of forms, sometimes featuring one part of the story, sometimes another. Liljeblat even goes so far as to relate to this the "strong-woman" motif, for example as represented by Brunhild or by Atalanta. The latter connection appears a little far-fetched; but it seems, on the contrary, quite reasonable to relate the story of Tobit to those which center round the bride who has a demon lover.

Liljeblat calls attention to a further common characteristic between the oriental and certain of the western types, a characteristic better motivated in the latter: the helper of the hero is a grateful dead man to whom the hero has done a favor. In the Tobit story this motif is not so well pointed up; it is Tobit's father who wins God's favor by his pious burial of his dead countrymen; in the western versions the hero is helped by a returned dead man whom he has buried.

Where Zabara got his apparently unique version of the Tobit story is a problem to which I do not know the answer. It is possible that, from its connection with the Hebrew liturgy, it found its way, in this abridged form, into the popular repertory.[58]

Gower [59] gives a very much abridged version based on the apocryphal account. The two medieval Hebrew texts translated by Gaster [60] are also essentially like that of the *Apocrypha.*

Tale fourteen is the familiar story of the Fox in the vineyard. There is no need to discuss at length here the parallels to this favorite Aesopian fable, familiar to us today through modern as well as the older writers. It may be noted, however, that in Zabara's story, as in that of Nicole Bozon (fourteenth century),[61] for example, it is the fox himself who eats

[58] Gaster (in the *Proc. Soc. Bibl. Archæol.*, XVIII, 219-20) calls attention to a shortened form of the story of Tobit, told, in regard to the paying of the tithes, in a medieval Hebrew sermon for the second day of Pentecost.

[59] Book VII (pp. 404-5, ed. Morley).

[60] *Proc. Soc. Bibl. Archæol.*, XVIII, 259-71; XIX, 27-38.

[61] No. 145 (pp. 184-85, ed. Meyer).

so much that he cannot get out through the hole by which he entered the garden. Sometimes, as in the *exemplum* of Jacques de Vitry (thirteenth century),[62] the fox lures the wolf into the vineyard (or the storeroom), and it is the latter who is trapped; while La Fontaine,[63] to cite a modern parallel, represents a weazel in a granary as the victim of greed.

The fifteenth and last tale in *The Book of Delight* has numerous parallels in Western-European literature.[64] It became so well known that it was even reduced to a proverb in many different languages,[65] a proverb to the effect that what the devil is unable to accomplish he delegates to an old woman to perform. Zabara's version is the earliest known so far. In the later versions which I have studied the motivation of the tale is less general than in *The Book of Delight*.

In these later versions the story runs somewhat as follows: A devil has spent a long time, usually several years, trying to bring discord into the relations of a conspicuously faithful and loving husband and wife. Unable to accomplish this, he turns over the task to an old woman, with the promise of a reward if she is successful. The old woman privately informs the husband and the wife in turn that she has proof that each is unfaithful to the other. She proposes to the wife to cure the husband of his infidelity by means of a hair, or hairs — usually to be made into a medicine — cut from his beard by the wife as he sleeps. She then tells the husband that his wife is planning to murder him in his sleep. He feigns sleep and sees his wife produce a razor, or some similar instrument, and approach his throat. He kills her with the razor, or, in some

[62] No. CXXIV (ed. Crane).

[63] Livre III, no. 17.

[64] Very extensive bibliographical references for this story are given by Wesselski, *Märchen des Mittelalters*, pp. 194-96. To these may be added the *exemplum*, given by title only, in Welter's edition of the thirteenth-century *Speculum laicorum*, no. 472. Knust (pp. 386-96) outlines several different versions. Hans Sachs (ed. Keller, in the *Bibliothek des literarischen Vereins in Stuttgart*, CXXV, 35-46) and Martin Luther (*Tischreden*, in his *Sämmtliche Werke*, ed. Irmischer, LX, 57) among others, both utilized this story.

[65] Knust (pp. 395-96) gives references for these proverbs in Dutch, Danish, Icelandic, Swedish, Latin, French, Italian, and German. See further, Wesselski, *Märchen des Mittelalters*, p. 196.

versions, beats her. In several of the accounts the devil gives the old woman her reward on the end of a long pole or from the opposite side of a stream, the fiend being afraid of a person so evil that she has outdone him in wickedness.

There are differences in detail in the various versions. In the *Conde Lucanor*[66] (fourteenth century), for example, the story is quite fully developed. The married pair are important people. The old woman takes service with the wife and gradually wins her confidence. The husband, after murdering his wife, is killed by his wife's relatives; a family feud results, and almost the whole of the town is wiped out. Here the old woman, instead of being rewarded by the devil, is taken to court and condemned to a horrible death. In the earliest German version,[67] that of *Salomon und Morolf*,[68] the happily-married pair are peasants. The wife alone is murdered here, and the old woman receives from the devil, as a reward, a pair of new shoes on a long pole. Another German version,[69] from a fifteenth-century manuscript, is essentially the same as the preceding, the only important differences being that the hairs are to be cut from a wart on the husband's throat and that the old woman is rewarded with money as well as with shoes.

In another group of stories the ending is not tragic. Étienne de Bourbon[70] tells the tale in a rather elaborate manner, the old woman going to some pains to produce evidence that the husband and wife are, respectively, unfaithful. There is no tragic ending, and the old woman is forced to confess. In the forteenth-century *Fabulae Adolphi*,[71] the married couple are peasants. The wife is merely beaten by her husband. The old

66 No. XLII (ed. Knust).

67 Earliest according to Knust, p. 393.

68 Pages 55-56, vv. 917-1008 (ed. von der Hagen und Büsching, I, last selection).

69 Ed. Pfeiffer, in *Germania*, III, 423-25; put into modern German by Wesselski, *Märchen des Mittelalters,* no. 5.

70 Ed. Lecoy de la Marche, no. 245; translated into German by Wesselski, *Mönchslatein,* no. XXII.

71 No. IX. Published by Polycarp Leyser, 2024-28 (ed. MDCCXXI); Wright, *Latin Stories,* Appendix II, 184-86.

woman receives her reward, in this case money alone. The version published by Haupt and Hoffman [72] also lets the wife off with a severe beating. The old woman is here rewarded with a pair of shoes.

John Herolt [73] (d. 1418) represents the wife as being killed by the husband, as in the versions previously mentioned; but his story differs from these in that the old woman is unaware that she is dealing with the devil. Here she receives her reward, of money, not on the end of a long pole, but from the other side of a river.

Zabara fits this story into the framework of his narrative by having Enan assume the rôle of the devil and tell the tale in the first person. The motive of Enan is not to ruin the happiness and the virtue of a certain godly couple, for the sake of earning the praise of his satanic master, but to cause strife in a peaceful town. The old woman is a washerwoman, and, as in the *Conde Lucanor*, she takes service with the wife of a great man. It is her idea, not the demon's, to bring about a general feud through the dissension of the husband and wife. The husband kills his wife, as in the first group discussed above; her kinsmen slay him, and the resulting feud causes the death of 220 nobles. There is no mention of a reward for the old woman. Of the versions outlined, that of the *Conde Lucanor* thus bears the closest resemblance to that of Zabara: there is no question of a reward, the old woman takes service with the wife, and there is a family feud. Zabara's story cannot, however, have been Juan Manuel's only source; for the latter contains the feature, common to the other versions, that the devil has been making it his special aim to disrupt the amicable relations of a particular married pair. Zabara's story, although it is the earliest version known, is clearly one adapted by him to the particular needs of his narrative; it cannot be the original source for the tale.

[72] No. 17. Edited also by Thoms* (cf. Knust, p. 392.)

[73] *Promptuarium exemplorum,** tit. *Matrimonium* (this version published by Wright, *Latin Stories*, no. C).

It has been pointed out [74] that the reward of a pair of shoes,[75] a customary betrothal gift in some regions, is an indication that the old woman became the bride of the devil.

Of the other tales contained in *The Book of Delight*, my investigation has revealed little or no trace in the literature of Western Europe. The themes of most of these stories — the faithlessness of woman, the fox's treachery, the single act of piety which saves the soul of an otherwise evil man — are prevalent in that literature. Yet the stories themselves I have not discovered there. With one or two possible exceptions, they would be quite as adaptable to western taste as those to which I have found occidental parallels, and I should hesitate to say that such parallels do not exist, either in the extensive *exempla* literature or in folklore. One thing, however, seems certain; these stories that have eluded me, if they were known at all in the West, were not so well-known as those that have been analyzed above, or they would have found their way into one or another of the popular medieval collections that I have studied. It is, besides, quite possible that Zabara has included in his work tales that never became known in the West.[76]

The first story in *The Book of Delight* tells how the fox duped the leopard to his death. It does not occur in the *Roman de Renard*; nor is it found elsewhere to my knowledge in the European fable literature. The same may be said of the second story, in which the fox slays the lion under pretense of curing a headache of the latter. There is, however, some resemblance between this tale and that of the crow and the eagle in the *Fables* of Odo of Sheriton.[77] In Odo's story, the crow, summoned by the eagle to cure the eyes of the latter, pretends to treat them with a healing herb. But the herb blinds the eagle, and the crow is thus enabled to eat his victim's young. Both

[74] By Wesselski, *Märchen des Mittelalters*, p. 196.

[75] Zabara's version does not contain this feature.

[76] Curiously, most of these stories, apparently unfamiliar to the West, would seem to have been almost equally rare in Jewish literature; whereas the rest have oriental parallels (see Davidson, pp. xlvii-lxvii, where the editor indicates some oriental parallels to Zabara's tales).

[77] Ed. Hervieux, IV, 204, no. XXIX ("De aquilo et corvo medico").

of the tales in *The Book of Delight* are quite similar in spirit to others which illustrate the treacherous character of the fox and which do occur in occidental fables.

The third story and the fourth are tales showing how a woman, through her folly or her misplaced ambition, brings death or disgrace upon her husband and, incidentally, upon herself. The third would seem to be of Mohammedan origin — at least it would have no point in a Christian country — for the *dénouement* of the plot is brought about by the circumstance that the hero, a silversmith, in making an image of the king's daughter, violates the law that "everyone who maketh an image or a likeness" shall have his right hand cut off. In other words, he has disobeyed the Mohammedan religious precept which forbids the representation of the human form in art.

The eighth tale is in the nature of a detective story, for it tells of the ingenious manner in which a judge confirmed his suspicions, arrived at analytically, that a certain man was guilty of burglary.

The fifth story is one of the countless variations on the theme of the faithlessness of woman. It starts out, however, rather like a whole class of stories in Western-European literature, in which a bet made regarding the fidelity of a certain woman, usually the wife or the sister of one of the wagerers, leads to an attempt to seduce her on the part of the other better.[78] In the stories of this group, however, the woman is in the end proved faithful. The contrary is true in Zabara's narrative. In the latter tale, a king, hearing his retinue praise the virtue of women, expresses his conviction that even the best of the female sex are untrustworthy. He proves his assertion by offering a merchant of well-known virtue the hand of his only daughter, if the merchant will first slay his own wife. The husband cannot bring himself to do this. When, however, the king proposes to marry the wife, also renowned for her virtue, if she will first murder her husband, the only thing that

[78] See the classification of these tales in the article by Paris, in *Romania*, XXXII, pp. 481-551. Cf. also Hulme, in *Modern Language Notes*, XXIV, pp. 218-22.

prevents her from committing the crime is the king's foresight in giving her a tin sword for the purpose.

The twelfth story is that of a paralytic who lives on the road to a graveyard and whom God permits to rise up and pray whenever the corpse of a righteous man is carried by; if the dead man has been wicked, the paralytic is unable to arise. On a certain day, as a respected and supposedly pious elder of the city is being borne to his grave, the paralytic finds that he cannot rise from his bed. On the following day, however, he is able to stand up and pray at the passing of the corpse of a butcher known to have been violent and sinful. Upon investigation, it is discovered that the butcher had one redeeming quality: he had always particularly honored and cherished his old father. The elder, on the contrary, who had led an exemplary life as far as anyone, including his wife, knew, had been secretly a heretic.

The only story I have found that in any way resembles Zabara's is an anonymous one published by Thomas Wright.[79] In the latter tale a thief, desiring in his old age to confess his sins, falls and breaks his neck as he is running after some monks to put this desire into execution (the monks, fearing some act of violence on the part of their pursuer, are fleeing from him). Later on, a certain monk sees the soul of the thief borne to heaven by angels; while that of a usurer, whose body is receiving honorable burial, is being tortured by devils. The only similarity between the two stories is the fact of the revelation through a miracle of the salvation of a man of evil life and the damnation of the soul of one who had been honored by his fellows. The theme is the same in both tales; but the stories are not otherwise similar. The same might perhaps be said of the many miracle legends where a sinner is saved by a single good trait.

The thirteenth tale is told so briefly by Zabara, and seems to have so artificial a connection with his main narrative that one is puzzled to interpret it. It appears almost like an inter-

[79] *Latin Stories*, no. CV. I do not know the source or the date of this story. The editor merely says (p. 236) that it is "from a ms. in private hands."

polation. As a warning to Zabara not to overeat, Enan tells him of the king who held a feast to celebrate the blooming of some lilies (or, perhaps, roses)[80] in the winter season. The king's daughter, who is heavy with child, approaches to smell one of the flowers, but as she does this, a serpent glides forth and frightens her so that her child is born and dies. The point of the story is obscure, perhaps because it is too greatly abridged. The details given suggest such folk-lore motifs as the white rose — if it was a rose — as the symbol of death on the one hand or of immortality on the other.[81] The immortality of the serpent is, according to Frazer, a "widespread belief." [82] There are, further, frequent references in European literature to the serpent hiding beneath flowers; for example, in John Lydgate [83] and in an anonymous Latin poem entitled *Peregrinus*,[84] but that would be quite a natural poetical conceit. I have discovered no occidental parallel to this story of the princess and the winter-blooming flowers, unless one finds the following *exemplum* of Jacques de Vitry [85] related to Zabara's tale: "I have heard," says the Frenchman, "of a certain serpent which carried a beautiful rose in its mouth. A certain person, noticing the great beauty of the rose, began to touch it and to smell its fragrance, and because he did not notice the poison, he died, infected by it. . . ."

The twelfth century, at the end of which Zabara lived, is one of the most interesting periods in the history of western medicine.[86] Medical theory and practice had in Christian

[80] Davidson (p. lxv) and Abrahams (in the *Jewish Quarterly Review*, VI, p. 527) translate "roses."

[81] Cf. Bolte und Polivka, III, 460, no. 203; Grimm, *Kinder- und Hausmärchen* (1856), p. 264; Gubernatis, II, 323 (*Rose*).

[82] Frazer, I, 49 ff.

[83] Book IV, vv. 2584-85 (ed. Bergen, Part II, p. 544).

[84] Published by Polycarp Leyser, Sect. XV, no. XXVI, pp. 2099-2120 (ed. MDCCXXI). The passage in question is v. 180 (p. 2107).

[85] Ed. Crane, pp. 65-66, no. 147.

[86] A good summary of the history of medieval medicine is given by Diepgen, II (*Mittelalter*). Of the numerous more exhaustive histories of medicine, the following may be mentioned: Daremberg, Puschmann und Arndt, Neuburger. A helpful bibliography is contained in Garrison, pp. 884-922. Two good short histories of medicine are those of Boinet, Singer.

Europe emerged from the cloister, where they had for several centuries been ensconced. The medical school at Salerno, founded in the eleventh century, had already in Zabara's time a rival in Montpellier. The profession of medicine in Christian countries was rapidly becoming secularized. Another significant fact is that, whereas those of Salerno still taught the theories which had been handed down more or less directly from the Greek and Roman writers on medical subjects, the later medical schools in the Christian countries adopted those theories in their Arabian dress. It was still Graeco-Roman medicine; it was Galen who was the great exponent of that medicine for the Arabians and who through them became so for the Christians. What appealed to both Mohammedan and medieval Christian in the Galenic system was not so much the great physician's really striking contributions to the knowledge of physiology and of anatomy, as the perfection of his philosophical concept of the structure and the functioning of the body as an evidence of the power and the goodness of God. Precepts drawn from this philosophical concept had prevented Galen from extracting from his observations many a scientific truth which he might otherwise have discovered. It was the corpus of these precepts that attracted the Arabians and those who professed the Scholastic philosophy, with the result that, even down to the eighteenth century, the progress of medical science was retarded by the authority of the name of Galen.

The Arabians were primarily responsible for this, and it was in the twelfth century that the works of their translators and commentators of Galen began to be widely known in the Christian West through Latin translations, made to a large extent by Jews. The authority of Avicenna came to rival that of Galen or Hippocrates, and it was not long before the works of a Johannitius, of a Rhazes, or of a Serapion were used as textbooks in the universities.

The Jews, not only through their translations, but also by reason of their wide reputation as physicians, were instrumental in this work of introducing Arabian medicine among European Christians.[87] There were, besides, Jewish writers on medical subjects; for example, Maimonides, who, however, was not so well known to the Christians as were some others.

The Arabians did more than merely adopt the results obtained by Galen. Some of their great physicians, while following his teachings, made further discoveries in the fields of anatomy or of experimental physiology. They did a great deal, also, to develop the knowledge of pharmacy. Hippocrates, although he advocated drugs when absolutely necessary in the cure of disease, had based his therapeutics upon the strengthening of the natural processes by diet, air, exercise and the like. Galen followed his master in this, but at the same time recommended the use of medicines to a far greater extent than did Hippocrates. The Arabians were expert chemists and they experimented more widely than others in the field of pharmacy.

Joseph Zabara, like most physicians of his time, followed the teachings of Galen. He was a conservative rather than an innovator. In his writings he accepts Galen, without modification, as the final authority and becomes wary when it is a question of the newer trend of practice. For example, he states unequivocally his faith in the Hippocratic principle of cure by natural methods. "Leave the drugs in the chemist's pot," he says, "if so thou canst heal thy patient with food." [88] Again, he believes in the prevalent practice of uroscopy as a means of diagnosis; but he cries out vehemently against the equally prevalent abuse of this method by the quack.[89] The quack was in the Middle Ages perhaps a greater menace to public health than he is today. Zabara was not alone in his protest. In the thirteenth century in France we find even the hack writer Rutebeuf [90] composing a parody at the expense of the herb vender of the market place.

Zabara probably wrote *The Seats of the Soul*, a short

[87] See pp. 6-7, and cf. Münz.
[88] *The Book of Delight*, p. 114.
[89] *Ibid.*, pp. 141-42.
[90] "Li diz de l'erberie," in *Rustebuef's Gedichte* (ed. Kressner), pp. 115-20.

medical work in verse, and it is possible that he is the author of another metrical composition entitled *A Treatise on Uroscopy.*[91] Besides this, as already stated, medical discussions occupy a considerable portion of *The Book of Delight.* In addition to the observations relating to that science, which are scattered throughout the latter work, the whole of Chapter IX is devoted to questions and answers on medical subjects. There are, furthermore, similar questions on pages 139-41, but these remain unanswered.

The medical theories professed by Zabara are, briefly, the following. As stated above, they are essentially those of the Galenic system. The basic principle, that of Hippocrates, is the humoral one: The body contains four humors: blood, phlegm, yellow bile and black bile.[92] These correspond respectively to the four elements: air, water, fire and earth. Galen's theory of the "spirits"[93] is outlined: the "soul" spirit[94] is situated in the brain; the "vital" spirit[95] resides in the heart; the "natural" spirit[96] is found in the liver. The first of these governs the five senses and the bodily motions; the second maintains life and gives man wisdom and discernment; the third, by controlling the distribution of the blood, nourishes the body.

Zabara has much to say about various parts of the body and their functions. He holds the theory, first propounded by Poseidonios in the fourth century,[97] that the brain is divided into three chambers (front, middle and back) containing,

[91] Davidson (pp. xcvii-xcviii) doubts that Zabara wrote the second of these two works. It was quite customary in the Middle Ages to compose medical as well as other scientific works in verse, in Christian countries also. Gilles de Corbeil (d. 1220), who lectured at Salerno and was physician to Philippe-Auguste, wrote two medical poems in Latin hexameters: one was on the *Urine,* the other on the *Pulse* (both edited by Choulant). The famous *Regimen sanitatis salernitanum* (twelfth century) was likewise in verse. Many more examples of similar works are extant.

[92] See *The Book of Delight,* p. 120; *The Seats of the Soul,* pp. 174-75. Zabara calls the yellow bile "red," and phlegm he designates as "white bile."

[93] This theory of Galen is succinctly outlined by Boinet, pp. 44-45.

[94] *Spiritus animalis.*

[95] *Spiritus vitalis.*

[96] *Spiritus naturalis.*

[97] See Diepgen, p. 6.

respectively, the imagination, the reason, and the memory.[98] The relative positions of these three faculties explain why one puts one's head forward to imagine, but back to recall, something: it is to bring the reason into conjunction with the proper faculty. Zabara explains the act of seeing by Galen's erroneous idea of two hollow perforated passages behind the eyes. Double vision he attributes to the disparity of these passages. Galenic also is his description of the heart as consisting of two chambers, one to contain the vital spirt, the other the blood.[99] In Zabara's rather detailed account of the digestive process he again closely follows Galen,[100] outlining the functions of the stomach, the liver, the spleen, the intestines, etc. Some of these descriptions are quite accurate. In regard to reproduction, he explains the likeness of the child to its father by the theory that the blood which becomes semen is drawn from all parts of the body.[101]

Concerning the cure of disease, Zabara gives some directions having to do with bleeding. He uses drugs warily [102] and puts his faith above all in proper diet. If it were not that the question of diet, as a preventive as well as a curative measure, so largely engaged the attention of both ancient and medieval medical writers, the reader of *The Book of Delight* would feel convinced that Zabara suffered from an obsession by the subject.[103] One has only to glance at the titles of the works composed by the great physicians from Hippocrates or Galen to Maimonides, and to call to mind such treatises as the *Regimen sanitatis Salernitanum*, to see the importance of the place given to the problem of diet before and during Zabara's time. One understands then that, whether or not a physician of the twelfth century had a personal preference for the subject, he would almost certainly treat it fully in his medical writings.

98 See *The Book of Delight*, p. 128; *The Seats of the Soul*, p. 171.
99 See *The Seats of the Soul*, p. 176.
100 Cf. the résumé of Galen's teaching on the digestive process, in Neuburger, I, 375-78.
101 See *The Seats of the Soul*, p. 176.
102 Cf. p. 32.
103 See *The Book of Delight*, pp. 48-51, 111-25, etc.

One further remark about Zabara's medical knowledge. He was apparently not a surgeon, for his extant works contain no references to that branch of medical science.

The Book of Delight has quite a long passage dealing with the subject of physiognomy.[104] Zabara's source seems to have been the chapter on physiognomy in the pseudo-Aristotelian *Secretum secretorum*, the authorship of which Zabara attributes to Plato.[105] The idea that character impresses itself upon the features, and also that the coloring, the size and the shape of these features is an index to a man's nature, had early suggested itself to the ancients. The theory was developed with enthusiasm by medieval writers. The earlier discussions of the subject were purely descriptive; later, the study of physiognomy was used to predict the future, and this branch became the more popular one.[106] Here again Zabara belongs to the older, conservative school: he merely tells what moral traits are indicated by certain physical characteristics; he does not speak of the human face as an index of the future.

Zabara evidently wished the reader to infer that he was versed in still other sciences, such as arithmetic,[107] geometry,[108] astronomy,[109] physics,[110] and phonology,[111] for he asks his demon-guide Enan pertinent questions regarding them. Since

104 See pp. 54-55.

105 Davidson (pp. lxxxii-lxxxv) discusses quite fully the sources and parallels to this passage of *The Book of Delight*. He indicates the reasons for thinking the *Secretum secretorum* to have been Zabara's source, and also the confusion which may have caused Zabara to attribute that work to Plato.

106 Foerster (II, Sect. V C, pp. 181-222) edits the passage from the *Secretum secretorum* and also a number of important later selections, in Greek, Latin, and Arabic, on the subject; besides an anthology of references to *physiognomy* in the works of the classical Greek and Latin poets and prose writers. Among the Arabian authors dealing with the subject may be mentioned Rhazes, *Physiognomy*, translated by Gerard of Cremona in the fourteenth century (Gerard's translation edited by Foerster, II, 161-79). The Christian "physiognomists" of the Middle Ages include Michael Scot (*De physiognomia et de hominis procreatione**) and Albertus Magnus (*De animalibus*, lib. i, Tract. ii, cap. ii-x).

107 See *The Book of Delight*, p. 138, question 8.

108 See *ibid.*, p. 137, questions 3, 4.

109 See *ibid.*, p. 137, questions 1, 2; p. 139, question 9.

110 See *ibid.*, p. 127, questions 5, 6; pp. 132-33, questions 24-27; p. 138, question 7; p. 140, question 16. Only the last two of these questions go unanswered.

111 See *ibid.*, p. 138, questions 5, 6.

Enan was, however, ignorant of the answers, Zabara is excused from demonstrating the extent of his own knowledge. From the rather detailed nature of the inquiries regarding lunar intercalation,[112] one would judge that he knew something of that part of astronomy, at least.

Not all the questions about physics are put to Enan; some of them are asked by Enan and answered by Zabara. Thus we find that the latter was familiar with Aristotle's observations on salt water, and more particularly with the peculiar character of the Dead Sea.[113] However, as Dr. Davidson shows, he would seem to be citing not Aristotle himself, but Rabbi Gershon.[114] Alexander Neckam (1157-1217), a contemporary of Zabara, also has a passage ("Quare aqua marina salsa sit") in his *De naturis rerum*[115] based, the author says, on Aristotle. A Christian writer of a little earlier date, Adelard of Bath (flourished *c.* 1120), gives in Question 51 of his *Quaestiones naturales perdifficiles*[116] an explanation of the saltness of sea water. Alexander Neckam's passage would seem to be an abridgement of this question. However, Zabara's explanation has only this statement in common with that of the two English writers: namely, that salt water is warmer than fresh water.

Adelard of Bath's thirty-third question has a closer parallel in *The Book of Delight*[117] than has the one just discussed. It is an explanation of why man's breath is cool under certain conditions and hot under others.

Scattered through *The Book of Delight*, and more particularly on pages 101-10, are many anecdotes and proverbs, a

[112] See *The Book of Delight*, pp. 138-39.

[113] See *ibid.*, p. 132.

[114] See Davidson, pp. lxxviii-lxxx. Dr. Davidson places side by side the corresponding passages concerning the Dead Sea from Aristotle, Zabara, and Gershon. The citation from Aristotle is taken from his *Meteorologica*, Book ii, Chap. iii. Similarly, Zabara derives from Aristotle his explanation of the formation of hail; but he does so by way of Gershon (see Davidson, p. lxxx).

[115] Liber II, cap. 1 (ed. Wright, p. 127).

[116] Questions 33 and 51 of this work are printed in full by Davidson, Appendix C, pp. cxvi-cxvii.

[117] Page 127.

large proportion of which are referred to one or another of the great "sages" of antiquity, Socrates, Aristotle, Diogenes, Hippocrates, etc. Dr. Davidson is of the opinion that Zabara's sources for these were almost certainly Arabic.[118] Some of the anecdotes, as Dr. Davidson also notes,[119] were familiar to medieval Christian writers as well. A few of these latter parallels may be mentioned. For example, the alleged sardonic remark of Socrates about the woman hanging from the fig-tree bough [120] is certainly related to the story told in the *Gesta Romanorum* [121] of the man who is found bewailing the fact that his three successive wives have each hanged themselves on a certain tree in his garden. An acquaintance asks the bereaved husband for three shoots from his tree. These are to be divided among the neighbors, for an obvious purpose.

Another anecdote related of Socrates by Zabara [122] is that of the scolding washerwoman who is compared by the philosopher to a thunderstorm. This is applied by Gower [123] to Socrates' own wife.

Two of the sayings attributed by Zabara [124] to Diogenes, are to be found, without any specific attribution, in the *Tractatus de diversis materiis predicabilibus* of Étienne de Bourbon.[125] These sayings illustrate the degeneration of noble blood. Petrus Alphonsus, in his *Disciplina clericalis*,[126] relates somewhat similar incidents of two poets and a king, incidents which recur, as would be expected, in the Old French metrical translation of that work of the converted Spanish Jew: *Le Castoiement d'un père a son fils.*[127] Curiously, however, it is the version given by Étienne de Bourbon, and not that by one who would presumably use the same sources as Zabara, that more

118 Pages xxxix-xl.
119 *Ibid.*, pp. xlii-xliii.
120 *The Book of Delight*, p. 66.
121 No. 33 (ed. Oesterley).
122 *The Book of Delight*, p. 67.
123 Pages 148-49 (ed. Morley).
124 *The Book of Delight*, p. 103, nos. 17, 18.
125 Ed. Lecoy de la Marche, no. 292.
126 Ed. Hilka und Söderhjelm (1911), *Exemplum* III, p. 9.
127 Ed. Barbazan et Méon, II, 68-70, vv. 130-92.

closely corresponds to the anecdote told in *The Book of Delight.* Both Étienne de Bourbon and Zabara relate how a man of humble birth aptly retorts on two occasions to one of noble lineage who reviles him: "I am the head of a noble line, thou the tail of thine"; and again: "I grace my family, thou disgracest thine." The latter witticism is more skillfully turned by Zabara than by the French preacher. In the account given by Petrus Alphonsus, only the general idea is the same; the incidents are quite different in detail.

The succinct moral precepts concerning preparation for this life and for the future life, included in *The Book of Delight*,[128] occur likewise in the *Disciplina clericalis*,[129] and in the *Castoiement d'un père a son fils*, [130] in words almost identical with those of Zabara.

The motif of the "wisdom-vendor" occurs in an anecdote of Zabara,[131] in the *Gesta Romanorum* [132] and in Étienne de Bourbon.[133] Bulaeus,[134] also, recounts a story of the founding of Charlemagne's palace school, a story revolving around the same motif. Except for the *Gesta Romanorum* and Étienne de Bourbon, where the stories are practically identical, these versions differ greatly among themselves. Zabara's seller of wisdom, as in the *Gesta Romanorum* version, offers the king three bits of wisdom for a stipulated price. But the three pieces of advice in no way resemble those in the other work: they are of a definitely personal nature; whereas, in the *Gesta Romanorum* they are general rules of conduct. Another difference is that in the *Gesta Romanorum* the king pays the price and subsequently puts his purchase to the test; Zabara's wisdom merchant, on the other hand, refuses to accept the payment offered, saying that he was merely trying to find out whether there was still any demand for wisdom in the market. We are

128 Page 106, nos. 52, 53.
129 Ed. Hilka und Söderhjelm (1911), p. 45 (following *Exemplum* XXVIII).
130 Ed. Barbarzan et Méon, II, 175, vv. 119-23.
131 *The Book of Delight*, p. 105, no. 45.
132 No. 103 (ed. Oesterley).
133 No. 81 (ed. Lecoy de la Marche).
134 This anecdote from Bulaeus is given in full by Davidson, p. xliii. Cf. also Laurie, pp. 41-42.

not given the opportunity of finding out the worth of his wares. Étienne de Bourbon's version is the same as that of the *Gesta Romanorum*, except for the fact that in the former mention is made of only one piece of wisdom instead of three. That one is identical with the first in the *Gesta Romanorum*.

The story about Charlemagne would seem to be an entirely independent one built around the "selling wisdom" idea — I leave out of account the possibility of regarding the incident as historic fact.[135] In this cheerful anecdote, two Scotchmen come to Aix-la-Chapelle and mingle their cry, "Wisdom for sale," with the other cries of the market place. Brought before Charlemagne, they inform him that their price for their wisdom is a place in which to teach, pupils, and a living wage. Thus was the palace school founded under Alcuin and one of the Scotchmen. The other was placed in charge at Pavia.

A parallel has been suggested,[136] in the *Gesta Romanorum*,[137] to Zabara's anecdote of the woman praying for the death of the king and the king's recommendation to her that she add to her prayer a request for a better successor.[138] However, the incident is approached from a different angle in the Latin *exemplum*; there, when all the Syracusans are hoping for the death of Dionysius, an old woman prays fervently that he may be allowed to continue to live. Her reason is that she has lived under two tyrants before him, each of the three worse than his predecessor, and she is afraid that a fourth one would be still more evil.

The saying in *The Book of Delight*,[139] that if a peacock be deprived of his feathers he will be no different from a plucked cock, is perhaps related to the fable of the owl, recounted by Nicole Bozon:[140] The parliament of birds asked the owl to become the consort of their king, the eagle, because the former had such a large head. "But if you pluck out my feathers,"

[135] See Laurie, p. 41.
[136] By Davidson, p. xliii.
[137] No. 53 (ed. Oesterley).
[138] *The Book of Delight,* p. 106, no. 51.
[139] Page 106, no. 59.
[140] Pages 74-75, Section 53 (ed. Meyer).

remarked the owl to the messengers, "my head will be no larger than yours." M. Meyer, the editor of Bozon's *Contes*, states that he knows of no parallel to this fable.[141] Perhaps Zabara's saying may be considered as such.

Some of the anecdotes and sayings just mentioned are found, almost verbally identical, in Diogenes Laertius, *Lives of Eminent Philosophers*; for example, Socrates's comparison of his wife's scolding to a thunderstorm,[142] and the remark of Socrates (ascribed by Diogenes Laertius [143] to Diogenes) about the woman hanging on a fruit tree. In addition, *The Book of Delight* contains certain other passages similar to those in Diogenes Laertius and ascribed in the Greek work to Diogenes: the anecdote of the inscription on the door, "Let Nothing Evil Enter," and the philosopher's uncomplimentary comment; [144] the sage's rebuke to the eater of olives in the tavern; [145] the warning to the harlot's child who was throwing stones;[146] and, finally, the incident of the archer with a bad aim.[147]

The Book of Delight is composed in the *Maqama* form; that is, it is written in rhymed prose interspersed with strict verse, the latter introduced by some such phrase as, "And thus hath the poet said." As regards the passages in strict verse, it is not clear whether Zabara is quoting some poet or writing a poem of his own. Rhymed prose is a form of writing unfamiliar to the English language and apparently unsuited to it. A few attempts have been made to employ it in English, but the effect is awkward and stilted.[148] The system consists in using rhyming words before natural pauses and without regard to the relative length of the intervals separating the rhyme words. This inequality produces a rather startling ef-

141 *Op. cit.*, p. 253.
142 Diogenes Laertius, I, 167 [ed. Hicks].
143 *Ibid.*, II, 53.
144 *Book of Delight*, p. 67; Diogenes Laertius, II, 41.
145 *Ibid.*, p. 109, no. 93; Diogenes Laertius, II, 53.
146 *Ibid.*, p. 103, no. 24; Diogenes Laertius, II, 63.
147 *Ibid.*, p. 103, no. 22; Diogenes Laertius, II, 69.
148 See, for examples of rhymed prose in English: Gollancz, *Tophet and Eden*; Abrahams, in the *Jewish Quarterly Review*, VI, pp. 522-24.

fect upon the unaccustomed ear of an English reader, but it is harmonious in Arabic or Hebrew.

The *Maqama* form was introduced into Greek by Menippus of Gadara. It is probably of oriental origin.[149] Mixtures of prose and poetry in the same composition are not unknown to European literature of the Middle Ages; for example, there is the thirteenth-century *Aucassin et Nicolette*.[150] Furthermore, Boethius' *Consolation of Philosophy*, a work particularly popular in the Middle Ages, has the same characteristic. Neither of these, however, has the recurrent phrase "And thus hath the poet said"; the portions in verse in the two works do not even purport to be the creation of a poet other than the author.

The present translator of *The Book of Delight* has rendered the rhymed prose into English prose and the strict verse, more or less closely, into English verse. The pseudo-Elizabethan English employed in the translation was chosen because it seemed best suited to the peculiar character of the Hebrew texts, which are full of Scriptural echoes and are most appropriately rendered by the language of the authorized version of the Bible.

The dedicatory epistles have been translated quite literally, line for line, the original possessing the same inconsistency in length as the translation. Zabara's dedication of his work to Sheshet Benveniste has all the fulsomeness characteristic of the days when the material rewards for literary effort must be secured from some wealthy and influential patron. It is nevertheless likely that Zabara was sincere in his praise of his benefactor, who was himself a writer worthy of admiration, and the composer of medical works.

The earliest known edition of *The Book of Delight* is that contained in a volume of works published in Constantinople in 1577.[151] Only two copies of this edition are extant, and

[149] See von Christ, 2. Teil, 1. Hälfte, p. 89: "Solches Stilgemisch [prose and poetry] in solcher Ausdehnung ist nicht griechisch, sondern orientalisch und gemahnt an arabischen *Maqamen*." Cf. further, Hadas.

[150] Edited by Suchier, among others.

[151] For a detailed description of the various editions of Zabara's works, see Davidson, pp. lxxxvii-xcviii.

both are defective. In 1865 Senior Sachs published in Paris an edition from a manuscript in the Günzburg library; this differs considerably from the Constantinople edition, but neither, apparently, gives the original version. The definitive edition is that published by Israel Davidson (New York, 1914). This is based on a comparison of the two previous editions. Dr. Davidson has, in his edition, divided the book into chapters with rubrics. This is the edition used by the present translator, who has followed the rubrics as well as the text of the editor. An edition and translation into Catalan has been published by Ignasi González-Llubera (Barcelona, 1931).

The Seats of the Soul was printed, from a corrupt manuscript copy, by S. G. Stern in his edition of the liturgy for the New Year (Vienna, 1859). Dr. Davidson has included a critical edition of *The Seats of the Soul*, from two manuscripts, in his edition of *The Book of Delight.*

The Treatise on Uroscopy, which is sometimes attributed to Zabara, is probably not by him.[152] Dr. Davidson printed it for the first time in his edition of *The Book of Delight.*[153] It is not included in the present volume because of the doubtful attribution. In any case the matter offers nothing new.

The foregoing study, brief though it is, adds definite proof to that which we already have, of a free interchange of ideas between East and West early in the Middle Ages. Not only do a large proportion of the tales told in *The Book of Delight* have numerous parallels in contemporary or nearly contemporary Christian literature, but there existed likewise a community of scientific knowledge, and similar anecdotes were recounted of the famous men of the past. Zabara's immediate sources may have been Arabic or Hebrew. Perhaps the ultimate source of the Christian parallels is oriental too. In matters of science, both East and West refer to Aristotle, to Galen, to Hippocrates, or to some later investigator along the way initiated by the ancients. Yet we know that Arthurian

152 See Davidson, pp. xcvii-xcviii.

153 Pages 169-73.

romances were translated into Hebrew,[154] and that the *Quaestiones naturales perdifficiles* of Adelard of Bath, for example, were put into that same tongue in the author's own century.[155] Knowledge was interchanged. If some of Zabara's tales do not have Western parallels, that is probably a mere matter of chance. The themes of these stories are quite similar to those of others that were adopted by the West. The very fact that apparently for no intrinsic, logical reason, some stories were not interchanged while others were, is in itself interesting. The foregoing study of Zabara's tales, then, brings forward clear evidence of the responsiveness of West to East in the twelfth century. This responsiveness was bound to be all the more real if there is no fundamental difference in spirit between the stories of which I have found traces in the West and those which apparently did not pass into Christendom. If, as I suspect, Zabara's sources were exclusively Arabic and Hebrew, the inference to be drawn is even more striking.

There is, further, the interesting fact that the mold into which Zabara cast his work was a favorite one also with his Christian contemporaries. The "framework" narrative, the contest of wit in the form of questions and answers, the moral tales and the proverbs, an exposition of physiology conceived as a hymn of praise to the Creator,[156] the mixture of prose and verse: all these things are typical, not of East or of West, exclusively, but of the Middle Ages in which Joseph Zabara lived.

[154] See Steinschneider, *Hebraeische Uebersetzungen*, pp. 967-69; Landau, p. xxi.

[155] Steinschneider, *Hebraeische Uebersetzungen*, p. 463, Section 275.

[156] *The Seats of the Soul.*

Joseph Ben Meir Zabara

THE BOOK OF DELIGHT

Chapter I

Zabara beholdeth in his dream a man exceeding tall, who doth then rouse him out of his slumber, and give him victuals to eat. But first he disputeth with him concerning prayer and food and wine.

There lived a man in the city of Barcelona whose name was Joseph ben Zabara. From his youth up had he dwelt at ease, in amity with his friends and comrades. All that knew him became his friends, and they that were his friends loved him; among them was he respected and esteemed, bound to all by ties of affection. He for his part honored and exalted them, served them and healed them. For those of them that were sick he compounded suitable remedies, in accordance with his knowledge and his skill. In his love and charity he busied himself with his patients whether old or young, and served them, and ministered to them. Everyone, then, loved Joseph and sought his company eagerly; but as Scripture hath it (Psalms 117:5), Joseph was sold for a servant.

Came then a night when I, Joseph, was sleeping upon my bed. My sleep was sweet upon me, for that alone was my portion of all my labor. Things there are which are for the soul a weariness but for the body restful; other things are weariness for the body but restful for the soul. But sleep bringeth rest at once to body and soul, as all men know well.

Saintly Hippocrates was once asked, "What is sleep?" "In sleep," he replied, "the highest virtues descend into the depths of the being, to provide refreshed vigor for the body." Furthermore, Aristotle hath said, "Natural slumber compriseth a remedy for every malady." And Galen, "Natural slumber increaseth vigor and minisheth the evil humors." And finally hath the wise Jahja ibn Maseweih said, "Sleep in season bringeth the body to healthfulness."

And it came to pass as I slumbered that I saw an appearance

before me in my dream, in the likeness of a man exceeding tall, who did then rouse me as is the wont of a man who arouseth another from his sleep. "Arise, thou son of man," quoth he. "Wherefore slumberest? Awake thee, and look upon the wine as it floweth red. Arise, and recline at my side and eat whereof I have brought thee, as my means did avail."

So I arose in haste, just as dawn brake, and I beheld wine and bread and viands before me, and a lamp burning in the man's hand, whereof the light shone into every corner. Then I spake and said, "What may these be, good sir?" "My wine," he replied, "and my bread and my viands. Sit thee down, and eat and drink with me, for I love thee as thou wert of my mother's sons."

But after that I had thanked him for the kindness of the honor he did me, for his love and for the generosity of his hand, I said, "Sir, I may neither eat nor drink until that I have prayed to Him that discerneth my way and maketh my footsteps firm and vouchsafeth unto me all my needs. For indeed the choicest of the prophets and the chief of them that were called, our teacher Moses, may he rest in peace, hath said (Leviticus 19:26): 'Ye shall not eat anything with the blood: neither shall ye use enchantment nor observe times.' Thereby did he admonish the children of Israel that they should not eat until that they had prayed for their souls, for in truth *the blood* signifieth *the soul.* And so hath Saul said (I Samuel 14:34): 'Slay them here and eat; and sin not against the Lord in eating with the blood.' Furthermore he that doth eat before he have offered prayer and supplication is called fellow to the Destroyer and a worker of divination.

"Aristotle too was asked whether prayer or victuals should have first place. 'Prayer,' he replied, 'for prayer is the life of the spirit and victuals are but the life of the body.' Furthermore, prayer and study are not possible for a creature that is sated and a paunch that is stuffed. 'Which is better,' a philosopher was asked, 'victuals or prayer?' 'Abundance of prayer is helpful,' he replied, 'abundance of victuals harmful.' And a certain wise man hath said, 'Prayer doth result in victuals.'

Lastly a certain sage of the Sages hath said, 'Prayer is like as the spirit which goeth upward, whereas victuals are like as the flesh which descendeth downward, even into the earth.' "

Then said the stranger, "Pray, if such be thy desire; do as is good in thy sight." So I bathed my hands and face, and prayed before the Lord. Then I ate of all that was before me, for his soul was become dear in my sight. In the midst of the food I would drink of the water of the fountain, but he rebuked me and said, "Drink of the wine, for compared to it even pearls are nothing worth, and it is indeed a delight to the eyes." "But," I said, "I take no delight in it nor do I desire to drink it, for indeed I fear it." And he said to me, "Wherefore dost thou hate it in thine heart? Surely it maketh glad and rejoiceth the heart of man."

And I replied and said, "I cannot drink it; for he that drinketh of it doth become drunken until that he is stranger to his own brethren. Wine blindeth the eyes, darkeneth the whiteness of teeth, causeth forgetfulness, and rendereth the wise soul foolish. It maketh the faithful speechless and robbeth the elders of their wisdom. It weakeneth the powers of the body and paralyzeth the members in their functions, for it doth disturb the sinews which control them. It occasioneth many maladies, such as paralysis and stuttering and apoplexy, which doth corrupt all the members of the body and their functions. It revealeth the secrets of bosom friends and causeth dissension between brothers. Yea, wine is treacherous and doth strip a man's garments upon a cold day. And so hath the poet sung for any man that lusteth after wine:

Friend, let not thine heart incline
To the sweet seductive savor
Of smoothly flowing ruddy wine,
For bitter is its flavor.

You may cherish it now above fine gold,
It is but a treacherous friend;
It will desert and forsake you in shivering cold,
Your coat from your back will it rend.

Again:

Guard thee well, beloved friend,
Lest to Bacchus thy neck thou bend;
Else thy competitor will drive thy trade
While yet thou slumberest in noonday shade.

And also:

Of pomegranate juice mayst thou sip;
It is sweet and gentle and mild.
But keep red wine far from thy lip;
It is raging and fiery and wild.

"Further, our master Moses, may he rest in peace, forbade the Nazarites all wine and strong drink, in order that they might not become unclean and desecrate the vows by which they were hallowed all the days of their separation. Furthermore the priests were forbidden to drink wine when they came into the sanctuary to minister."

Then did the man's wrath kindle, and he said, "Wherefore and why dost thou reproach wine and revile it and slander it, not slightly but with vehemence, and recall its defects and deny its virtues? Dost thou not know, hast thou not heard, that wine begetteth gladness and banisheth sorrow and sighing? If any one be afflicted in soul, he may drink and forget his misery. Wine assisteth, furthermore, in the digestion of food, and availeth to assuage pain better than doth rest, it causeth diseases of the nose to depart, and is salutary for maladies of the intestines. It causeth the urine to flow, if it be restrained, it maketh a weak heart firm, and riddeth the kidneys and the veins of humors. It is excellent for arousing appetites, and awakeneth generosity in the heart of a niggard. It prolongeth a man's prime and deferreth his old age; it sharpeneth the wits, maketh the face to shine, and brighteneth the senses. And furthermore our sages — may their memory be for a blessing — have said, 'Wine and spices make a man open-minded.' And because of the sin which he sinned against his own soul in vowing abstinence from wine, Scripture commanded the Nazarite to offer two turtles or two young pigeons to expiate for his sin in afflicting his own person. Yea, and the poet hath sung:

Two fires there be of foaming liquids holden,
Of warfare grim the one, the other in chalice golden.
This one compounded of blood and tears,
A hero's glory, a mother's fears.
The other a sweet essence with genial flame
Kindled by friendship and love's great name.

And again:

As rise in heaven the shining planets
So in our hands rise shining goblets;
But setting stars to westward descend
While descending cups in our bellies end.

And also:

They shall miserably moan and grievously sigh
For despising the fruit of the vine;
The abstaining Rechabites shall wretchedly die
Of diseases fell and malign.

Like profitless water shall they be neglected
This gloomy folk, dour, severe;
In disdain, yea blasphemy, have they rejected
What God and man doth cheer.

Then said I unto him, "Seeing thou hast freely proffered thy kindness, let not thy wrath be kindled. The ancient physicians, who were wise and prudent, prescribed that water be drunk at the time of eating for that it is heavier than wine, and by its weight causeth the food to descend to the uttermost parts of the stomach, whereby digestion is improved by reason of the proximity of the heat of the liver, which lieth underneath and lendeth its aid. But an hour or two after eating they prescribed that a little wine unmixed with water be drunk, to augment the natural heat and assist the digestive powers."

"Truly hast thou spoken," said he, "and I too adhere to thy discourse, for in truth little availeth little and much harmeth little."

Chapter II

The stranger declareth his name to be Enan Hanatas, the son of Arnan Hadesh, and seeketh to persuade Zabara to forsake his own country and accompany him to a place where his wisdom will be properly recognized. Zabara feareth to follow after him and relateth many parables to show the cause of his fear. Finally, however, he is convinced and will go.

And it came to pass after that I had eaten and drunk with him that I asked concerning his place and his name, saying, "Prithee, good sir, now that thou hast honored me and given me to eat of thy bread and victuals and mine heart hath drunk of thy dear love, tell me pray, what is thy purpose and whence comest thou, what is thy country and of what people art thou?" And he answered and said to me, "I come from a distant land, from pleasant and fruitful hills; my wisdom is as thy wisdom, my people as thy people and my laws as thy laws. My name is Enan Hanatas, son of Arnan Hadesh." I said to myself, "Surely this is a wonderful and awful name. Never before have I heard its like."

He said to me, "Thou mayst not know the secret of my name until that thou hast become my guest and comrade. Come with me from this land and I will tell thee all my secret lore; leave this spot, for here they appreciate neither thy worth nor thy skillful wisdom. I will take thee to another place, in which thou wilt find great delight; a place choice and good, like a fruitful garden, and they that people it are lovable and pleasant and exceeding wise."

And I said to him, "But, good sir, how may I forsake my house and abandon my heritage and depart from my native land wherein my abode is fixed, where dwell gentle folk, noble and princely, and wise sages who possess understanding of all matters? The greater among them graciously do me honor, and the lesser attend me for their own honor. As long as I shall live they will bear me on the pinions of their love and when I am dead their physicians will embalm me. And the sage hath said, 'If thou dwellest in a place in peace and security, if the spirit of the ruler rise up against thee, yield not thy place.' The spirit of the ruler is the evil inclination of man, which doth beguile him, and turn him whithersoever it will. Furthermore the Arab hath said, 'He that changeth his place, his fortune too is changed.' "

But he mocked and said, "The sage hath said, 'He that doth lean on his own knowledge and wisdom will stumble by his speech and perish by his counsel.' What will it profit thee after thy death whether they embalm thee skillfully or tear thee in pieces? Why dost thou speak without counsel and without wisdom, being a man of understanding and discernment? Surely thou knowest that thy beginning is of the earth and thy end vermin and corruption. What will myrrh and cinnamon profit thee when thou hast departed to the night of desolation? Thou wilt not ascend to Arcturus but in Sheol thou wilt wither of rot as a garment which hath been eaten of moths. Cease from words of vanity, for neither by withes nor by chains are thy feet bound. Rouse thyself to words of spirit, come with me to security and tranquillity. If thou hast found honor in thine own place and art favored of the many among thine own people, wherefore shouldst thou withhold from coming with me, to show thy pleasantness and to cause thy name to be remembered? They say that the man who dwelleth in his own city, even if it should please the king to do him honor, he will not perceive his glory nor recall his name or fame until that he have removed to another land, and there become honorable and glorious, above the exalted ones of the city. For that man who goeth not forth to journey among his fellow men, his blood is on his own head. Can the flower grow without water (Job 8:11)? But that one is as spilt water which cannot be gathered up again (II Samuel 14:14). In the course of time worthy men remove to waters more pleasant. Furthermore the Arab hath said, 'Every journey and every change doth cause blessing and salvation.' "

Even as he was speaking to me I sighed deeply and my head was downcast to the earth; neither peace nor calm was mine. Said he to me, "Wherefore dost sigh and why doth not sorrow depart from thy heart? Reveal unto me thy heart's secret and that which is buried in thy bosom; perhaps I can banish the sorrow from within thee. For the Arab hath said, 'He that revealeth his secret sorrow to a comrade dear to his heart banisheth a part thereof, ofttimes the greater part.' " But I replied to him, "That which is in my heart and inmost thoughts I cannot utter with my lips, for I am abashed and ashamed, and therefore am I become silent and speechless for revealing to thee that which is hidden and which weighs upon my heart and my thoughts."

He then said to me, "Lo, I adjure thee by thine own and thy fathers' souls, tell me all thy thoughts."

And I said to him, "After that thou hast adjured me, and satisfied me with the honey of thy speech, I will reveal my secret before thee; let it but not provoke thy wrath." And he said to me, "Speak thy wish to the full, for in my sight thy lips drop myrrh."

I then replied and said, "Wise Plato hath said in his book on Physiognomy, that he whose countenance is ruddy as flame hastes and is hasted and is prone to prevarication. He whose eyes are sunken and quick to behold and perceive, that man is cunning and wily and of many devices. He whose eyebrows are abundant and shaggy, his speech is heavy and he is a man of grief and sorrow. And if his nose is in part thin, but his nostrils are full and large, he is a contentious man, full of dissension and quarrelsome. He whose forehead is curved and inclines to the sides of his face, that man is tempestuous in word and deed. If his lips be large and thick he is dull, evil by nature, and contentious. He whose ears are large is simple and full of folly. He whose neck is short is a deceiver, every man's adversary and enemy. He whose abdomen is large and whose ribs are well covered with flesh, his folly will neither depart nor minish. A thin shoulder is a sign of an empty spirit.

A short palm is a sign of defective knowledge. Every tall man is a fool, sinful in speech, blind and a follower of lustfulness; for being over tall his heart cannot be wide but must needs be strait, and since of the two chambers of the heart one is too strait to contain the blood which is his aliment and the marrow of the brain is sustained only by the remainder, both organs are weakened: the discernment of the heart and the understanding of the brain are both diminished. Furthermore, there being a more distant expanse between the brain and the heart, discernment and understanding cannot be quickly conjoined and therefore the tall man's knowledge is ever wanting."

When he heard this matter, that the knowledge of tall men is short, he uttered a great and bitter cry, saying, "Now I know that thou art seeking a pretext against me and art simulating in all thy speech."

I said, "I have also not forgotten and indeed know very well the characteristics of short men. For since their members are slight and short and the traits of the soul follow after the nature of the body and the limbs, short men display this same divergence. Nay, I am well aware of it. But I perceive that it behooves me to speak only of tall men seeing that thou art such. And of the indications I have mentioned, I recognize all in thy face. Therefore do I tremble and fear to go with thee and to follow in thy footsteps, lest there befall me what befell a certain leopard with a fox."

"What pray," said he to me, "was this happening you speak of?"

I replied: "A leopard once lived in content and plenty: ever he found easy sustenance for his wife and children. Hard by there dwelt his neighbor and friend, the fox. The fox felt in his heart that his life was safe only so long as the leopard could catch other prey. 'If other prey should be wanting for a single day he will seize me in his might and slay me in the strength of his wrath, for he is in truth but shameless and he will apportion me unto himself and his sons as viands. Surely

I must bespeak him cunningly and beguile him with words of deceit; mayhap I shall prevail by wile and cast from my neck the yoke of his burden. "Before the evil cometh," the sage hath said, "counsel is good, but after trouble hath arrived it is but vain." Therefore will I remove him from my dwelling place and cause him to depart from my habitation. I will banish him from his place ere he swallow me, and cast him from his station ere he cast me down and devour me. Perhaps I can lead him in the path of death, for have not our sages of blessed memory declared, "If one come to slay thee, arise thou betimes and slay him?" '

"On the morrow then it came about that the fox came to the dwelling of the leopard in order to fulfill his purpose. The leopard addressed him, 'Whence comest thou?' Reynard replied, 'From a place of amazing beauty and goodness, a place of gardens and orchards, of lilies and myrtles, of turtle doves and pigeons, of hinds and does, of conies and wild goats and asses. They bray amongst the bushes and the fatted oxen lie in the grass. And I have come to give thee the tidings and to lead thee unto that place, for this place is despised and rejected and not fat but lean.'

"The leopard spake, 'Show me this place, for I am indeed eager to see it.' And he led him to that place, but the leopard knew not it was to be at the cost of his life. When he saw the comeliness of the place and its delights, the pleasantness of its situation, its approaches and its avenues, its woods, its shrubs, its herbage, its orchards and myrtles, its hinds and does, he rejoiced exceedingly and was filled with gladness and delight. The fox said in his heart, 'How many joys have been turned to sorrows! This, God willing, shall be added to that number.' The leopard said, 'Now do I know that thy soul is bound fast unto mine, and that love of me is cherished in thy heart, for by reason of the love thou hast for me hast thou chosen a place whose like mine eye hath never beheld nor hath mine ear heard report thereof. Be thou richly blessed, good and beloved sir. I will but go and take counsel with my wife and reveal unto her my secrets, for she is my comrade and the wife of my youth.'

"But the fox feared her, for that she was clever, and of sound sense, and subtle. So he said, 'Take heed of a woman's counsel, for woman is evil and bitter in spirit and hard. Her heart is of flint, an accursed plague is she in the house. Wise and understanding men heed not their wives, for they are of light mind. The sage hath said, "Guard against their love; ask their counsel and do the opposite." Whoso heeds them and follows after them brings it about that both he and they are consumed in flames.'

"The leopard replied and said, 'Nevertheless it is incumbent upon a man and by statute ordained, that he take counsel of the wife of his bosom. Furthermore the sage hath said, "Take counsel with thy brother or with thy friend, and thy paths will be made firm." '

"The fox then said, 'How much have I counseled thee and taught thee and instructed thee and commanded thee, yet have I not found thee one who hearkens! Surely the prophet hath said (Micah 7:5) "Keep the doors of thy mouth from her that lieth in thy bosom." '

"The leopard then replied, 'Truth is with thee in all that thou hast spoken, for at times woman makes of sweet bitter and of bitter sweet. But I will go and ask her, and if she forbid me I will not hearken to her counsel.' The fox said, 'So be it then, go in peace and I will wait until thou return hither.'

"Then the leopard went to his house, rejoicing and glad of heart. His wife addressed him, 'What is this joy wherewith thou art rejoiced and this gladness which shines forth in thy countenance?' To her he replied, 'My friend the fox, whose love for me is without let or deceit, has shown me a place spacious and secure for my dwelling. All that see it covet it and all that hear of it speak its praises; it is my purpose to remove hence and to dwell yonder.' 'Why and wherefore?' said his wife. He replied, 'Because our place is strait and our abode scant, and day by day our prey minishes and here bread nor meat suffices us. But there we shall find all our wants; we shall eat according to the pleasure of our hearts.'

"But his wife replied, 'Beware of the fox, of his gifts and his offerings, for he counsels for his own advantage. The sage, furthermore, hath said, "Two there be of the little folk of the earth, yet they are great in subtlety and cunning."' He inquired, 'And who may they be?' She replied, 'The serpent and the fox: They are the humblest of creatures, and are yet filled with guile and deceit. Surely thou hast heard what the snake did unto Adam and Eve, how the serpent did beguile them, and dissuade them from the commandments of their Creator, until that he brought them unto the gates of death? And hast thou not heard how the fox bound the lion by his cunning and slew him by his guile?'

"Then said the leopard to his wife, 'And how was the fox so confident as to approach a lion? Did not dread restrain him?' She replied, 'The lion loved the fox with all his heart, and advantaged him and befriended him, but the fox had small faith in him and plotted to slay him, for in truth he feared him greatly. Once on a day then, the fox came to the dwelling of the lion and was in great pain and cried out. The lion addressed him, "What ails thee, beloved of my soul?" And the fox replied, "A great pain hath seized my head." The lion asked, "And what may be done for thee, to assuage thy pain?" And the fox replied, "I have heard it said of the physicians of Araby that they prescribe that they who suffer from aches of the head be bound hand and foot, which doth then relieve them of their pain." Then said the lion, "I will bind thee, as thou sayest; mayhap thy pain will be eased by thy bonds." The lion took a forged chain and bound the fox hand and foot. The fox then said that his pain was departed, and the lion loosed him; nor did the pain return. Then it came to pass after a number of days that the lion found a great ache in his head, for so is his custom and wont, and he went to the fox and said to him, "Dear brother, my head is seized of a great pain, so that I am like to pray for death. Do thou quickly bind me with thy chain, both hand and foot. Mayhap my ache will be assuaged, even as befell thee." So the fox took fresh withes and bound him well and went from him and forsook him. Then he brought great stones and smote him upon the head and slew him.

" 'Perhaps that which befell the lion will befall thee also — forfend it Heaven — for his heart is but for guile, for wherefore chose he not that place for himself, to be his abode and his delight and his pleasure? Therefore do I tremble before him lest he take us in his snare and cause us to wander from this place to our hurt.'

"But the leopard spoke to her: 'Silence! for thou speakest as one of the shameful women! Be not bold to answer my words, for full oft have I tried him, yet never have I found dross in the pure silver of his love.' But she said, 'Hearken to my voice and abide in thy home, and destroy not thy seat and thy heritage.' But he would not hearken to her counsel, to her hurt and to his own.

"And the leopard went and returned to the fox and said, 'Lo, thy counsel is good and true, and thy love is fragrant with myrrh and frankincense. But my wife is not willing to follow after me, nor will she hearken to my words.' And the fox said, 'I tremble for thee, lest that which befell the silversmith befall thee also.' The leopard inquired, 'What happening was that?'

"And the fox narrated: 'There was once a silversmith in the land of Babylonia who was exceedingly skillful in the working of gold and of silver. One day as he was plying his work his wife said to him, "If thou wilt but hearken to my counsel and do as I bid thee I will make thee rich and increase thy glory and thy repute." He asked her, "Prithee, and how?"

" 'She said to him, "Lo, our lord the king hath but one daughter, whom he loveth as his own life and keepeth as the apple of his eye. Every day she doth come before him and doth sit at his right hand. And now hearken to my voice and fashion for her a silver image of her dear self; let it be beautiful and of pure silver. I will bestow it upon her as an offering and engage that there will ensue for thee wealth and honor and tranquillity." And the silversmith in his folly and want of sense hearkened to the voice of his wife and made an image comely and precious, and sent it to the princess by the hand of his wife. And it came to pass when she saw the image that she rejoiced exceedingly in its beauty, and she clothed the silversmith's wife with her mantle and gave her her earrings and bracelets. The woman returned to her house, rejoicing and exultant over her plan. When he saw her her husband asked, "What was thy fortune and how did the matter fall out?" And the woman replied, "See my mantle, my earrings, and my bracelets: all this the princess gave me." Her husband said, "And where is the wealth and the honor thou didst speak of? Art then in want of mantles and earrings and bracelets? Many and many times the value of these things thou hast received did I esteem that silver image."

" 'When morning came the princess showed the silver image to her royal father. The king then asked, saying, "Who made this image and gave it to the maid?" His servants replied, "A certain artisan made it, whose skill in the working of silver and gold is without equal in the land, and he did send it to the king's honored daughter, that it should become the most precious of all her ornaments." But the wrath of the king was kindled against the image which he saw in his daughter's hand, and he said, "Hasten and cut off the right hand of that artisan; for so is the law for everyone who maketh an image or a likeness." And they hastened and cut off his hand and divested him of his glory. The poor man humbled and sorrowing, with head downcast, returned to his house filled with bitterness and wormwood, and mourned. With a soul sore vexed he cried, "Unto you, O men, do I call: take ye heed lest ye hearken to the counsel of your wives, and stop your ear against their whispering, lest there befall you what befell me, for the counsel of my wife hath humbled my glory and cut off mine hand and corrupted my splendor." He continued in his crying day by day until that his gall was burst and his liver was spilled to the ground in his passion.'

"When the leopard heard the words of the fox he trembled exceedingly and said, 'Surely it behooves every man to beware the counsel of his wife.'

"The fox continued, 'A man who taketh counsel of his wife may suffer that which befell the woodcutter.' The leopard inquired, 'What, pray, was the story of the woodcutter?'

"The fox said: 'There was once a man in Damascus who was exceedingly skillful in the hewing of wood. One day he was preparing his logs with his two hands, being preoccupied with his affairs, and his wife was spinning beside him. She said to him, "My father, may his memory be for a blessing, was much more skillful at this trade than art thou. For he used to plane his logs with both his hands; when the one grew weary he labored with the other. But thou canst plane with thy right hand only." He replied to her, "No artisan or laborer may do his work but with his right hand only, except for the left-handed man, for in that case his left hand serves instead of the right." But she answered him, "By thy life, do but make trial of it and see whether thou canst not work with thy two hands as my father was wont to do." The simpleton then raised his left hand with his ax in order to smite the log, but smote instead the thumb of his right hand and cut it off. In a great rage he rose up and smote his wife's head with the ax, and her skull was crushed and she died. The matter became known in the court of justice, and they took the woodcutter and they brought him without the city and stoned him with stones.

" 'Therefore do I declare unto thee that all women are deceitful; they ensnare the lives of all. I shall relate to thee a little of their deceitfulness and their shamefulness.

" 'There was once a king of the kings of Araby who was wise and understanding and just, and who had sitting before him always wise and understanding counselors. One day they began to speak of the praises of women and of their virtues, and of their great wisdom and their patience. The king said to them, "Cut short your talk and restrain your words, for never hath there been seen or reported a woman who was good and virtuous, endowed with understanding and knowledge. Their love is only for their own benefit and their own pleasure; they have no government over their desires and they sin against themselves." Then his wise men said to him, "Let not the king say so, for there are indeed women that are wise and understanding, virtuous and faithful. They love and honor their husbands, find covering for their households and sustenance for their sons and daughters; in them there is neither fault nor disrepute." The king replied, "I shall give you a sign for my saying and a mark for my speech. Lo, this city is exceeding great: spread ye abroad therein and see whether ye can find a single woman endued with the virtues ye spake of and the qualities ye mentioned."

" 'And they sought and found in that city a woman of great reputation, modest and virtuous and wise, comely as the moon and clear as the sun. Her husband was a merchant, a man of great substance who pursued favor and sought goodness. The wise men returned their answer before the king, saying to him. "Lo, we have found a wise and understanding woman, free from fault or deceit, without willfulness or guile; and she is married of a husband."

" 'The king sent to summon the woman's husband and he came before him and made obeisance. The king cleared a place for him and caused him to sit down, and said to him, "There is a secret matter I would discuss with thee." He replied, "Speak O King, for thy servant hearkeneth to the voice of his lord." The king said to him, "I have a daughter lovely and good, mine only child. I do not desire to give her to a prince or noble, for I cherish her in my heart. But I seek for her a good and faithful man who is free from the iniquity of the times, that he may love her and honor her and bear her upon his shoulder, that he may adorn her with garlands, deal with her with a cheerful countenance, and maintain her in gentleness and loving kindness. There have come to mine ears thy many praises, thine excellent qualities and thy good deeds, and I desire to give my daughter to thee. But I cannot give her unto one who hath a wife; do thou slay thy wife this night and on the morrow I shall give thee my daughter to wife." The merchant replied, "My lord the king, who am I and what is my life that I should be son-in-law to the king? In good truth, I am not worthy to tend thy sheep." The king said, "Thee do I choose, for thou art my desire and my delight and without thee no man shall raise his hand or his foot in all my kingdom." The man replied, "But my lord the king, how can I slay my wife when she hath been with me these fifteen years? Of my bread doth she eat and she drinketh of my cup. She is my heart's delight and my joy. She doth love me and honor me, she watcheth over me and doth minister to me; mine honor is augmented in her eyes daily and never minishes, and I am preserved from every evil thing." But the king said to him, "Hearken to my voice and slay her, for by her death great honor will accrue to thee, for I will raise thy head above all the nobles of my kingdom and thou wilt rule over all that thy heart desires." The man replied, "I will make trial and see whether I may do this base deed."

" 'And he went out from before the king in sadness and sorrow, and the blood of his liver dropped with his grief.

" 'So he came to his house, and when he beheld his wife his sighs increased and his sorrow redoubled. His wife addressed him, "My good and pleasant lord, wherefore is thy countenance mournful?" But he refrained him and said to her, "May the Rock ward you from death and destruction: naught doth trouble me and naught but good is in my heart."

" 'And it came to pass in the night, when she was sleeping upon her bed, that he arose in confusion of heart to slay her. He took his sword in his right hand and a lamp in his left, and removed the covering from upon her. But when he saw her lying asleep, with her two babes at her breast, he took pity upon her and said, "Woe is me, how can I slay her, whither can I take my shame, who will bring up my children, who are the very apple of my eye? Surely it is but the multitude of my transgression and of mine iniquity." And he returned the sword to its sheath, and his soul was melted in sorrow, and he said in his heart with his eyes running tears, "Lo, my wife is better than all the kingdoms. Cursed be all kings, for they do but pursue after their own desires, and seduce the hearts of men with their vanities and pour waters of sorrow with the wine of their joy." And he ascended her couch and lay by her and kissed her and put his left hand under her head and embraced her.

" 'And it came to pass in the morning that he rose up and went to his storehouse to transact his business. The king awaited him, and when he tarried, sent messengers to come before him and to cause him to hasten and to know what detained him. When he saw the king's messenger his anxiety was great. He trembled and his heart was sore afraid.

" 'When he came before the king, the king asked of him, "What hast thou done? Hast thou slain her?" "Nay, my lord," he replied, "for love of her and pity of her overcame me"; and he related all that had befallen when he took the sword to smite her. Then did the king rebuke him saying, "Get thee from my sight and never look upon my face more, for thou art in no wise a man, but thy heart is as the heart of women." The man went from the king's presence rejoicing greatly in the king's anger and in his rebuke.

" 'And it came to pass toward evening that the king sent one of his servants to fetch the wife of the man secretly. And he went and brought her unto him and when the king beheld her he marveled at the comeliness of her appearance and the splendor of her face and form. He addressed her saying: "Lo, I have heard of thy wisdom and of the comeliness of thy conduct, and from the day of my hearing thy report there hath burned in my heart the fire of thy love, which hath drawn my soul with the bonds of desire. And now it is my pleasure to take thee to wife, and the kingdom shall be thine for a heritage. However, I may not take a woman that hath a husband, lest it be for a reproach. Go thee, and slay thine husband this night, and afterwards will I take thee and do for thee all thy heart may desire." And the woman replied in gladness of heart and in joy, "I shall do the king's bidding and I shall become his handmaiden." The king said, "But thou shalt be my wife and all my wives shall be thy tirewomen and my concubines thy handmaidens." And the king gave her a sword forged of tin, for he knew the weakness of a woman's wit. He said, "Lo here is my sword, a blade exceeding keen; do thou but smite him once; thou needst not repeat the stroke, for he will nevermore be able to rise." She took the sword and went to her house, all but skipping for joy.

" 'She prepared her meat and mingled her wine and brought forth her viands and arrayed her board. Her husband returned home to eat and to drink with his sons and with his wife, and at night she caused him to drink of the wine and made him drunk and lifted him to his bed and caused him to lie down. When it was yet night and he was in his drunkenness, slumbering upon his couch, she arose and took the sword and smote his head and thought that the metal had pierced his very life. But the sword of tin bent back, and he awoke from his slumber and was somewhat aroused from his drunkenness, and he cried out and said to his wife, "Who hath roused me from my slumber and who hath smitten me upon the head?" When the woman saw that he was awake and that her sword had left him uninjured, she was sore dismayed and her heart melted within her with the greatness of her dread and her trembling; her very soul all but left her body. She said, "Dear one, beloved of my soul, lie down and return to thy slumber, perhaps it was in thy dream that thou sawest one smiting thee." So he returned to his sleep, and availed not to open his eye, for he had not yet roused him from his wine. But his wife's anxiety increased without measure. She awaited in trembling until the dawn broke, then she arose to go about her tasks and to order her household, to atone for her shame for the evil deed that she had wrought; she set about to prepare the pottage for her husband as had ever been her wont.

" 'The king awaited her coming, but as she came not he

bade that she be fetched. When she came before him the king said to her, "Hast thou wrought the deed agreed upon between me and thee, or did thine eye take mercy upon him?" She replied, "My lord the king, I did thy bidding, but thou hast frustrated thy good plan and made it vain and nothing worth; for when I upraised thy sword against him, lo, thou hadst weakened it." And she related to him that which she had done and the iniquity that she had wrought. Then the king sent to summon her husband and said to him: "Do thou declare to these wise men that sit before me all that befell with thy wife; withhold no word." Thereupon he related all that had befallen between him and his wife. Then the king bade the woman tell all that had befallen her with her husband, and she did so. Then did the king speak to his wise men, saying: "Surely this is the saying that I spake to you when I bade you restrain your words." They replied, marveling at his wisdom, "With thee is the right; what is there for us to say? Surely our lord is wise as an angel of the Most High."

" 'Socrates, the divine philosopher, also, in the abundance of his wisdom and the greatness of his piety, hated women and loathed to look into their countenances. His own wife was spare and short, and when his disciples asked of him, "How came it that such a man as thou art should wed such a woman as this?" he replied, "I have chosen the least of the evil." One day as he was walking with his disciples in the cool of the day there passed before him a woman of comely figure and beautiful appearance, and one of his disciples gazed at her. Socrates said to him, "Woe is thee, wherefore dost thou gaze upon her?" The disciple replied, "Not for love nor for desire do I gaze, but to behold in her form the craftsmanship of the Creator." The master said, "Turn her inside out; then wilt thou understand her ugliness." Another time he was walking upon the way and he saw a woman hanging from a fig tree. He said, "Would that all the fruit of this tree were the same." And once he was walking with his disciples by the banks of a river, where a certain woman was washing clothes.

She cried out upon him, and cursed him, and reviled him, and heaped him with abuse; then she threw of the water upon him and drenched him. He said, "Surely she hath cast her lightning and hurled her thunder, and now she bringeth forth rain."

" 'Again, one of the great men built him a new house and wrote over the lintel, "Let no evil enter here." Diogenes, the philosopher, passed and saw the inscription, and then wrote underneath, "And how will thy wife enter?" Further, when one man reported to another, "Thine enemy hath perished," he replied, if thou hadst said, "He hath taken a wife," I had been better pleased.'

"Said the fox to the leopard, 'All this have I told thee that thou mayest know it behooveth no man to have trust in his wife all the days of his life, nor even after his death.'

"But the leopard said, 'During his life, to be sure, she may indeed deceive him, but what power hath she over him after that he hath died?' Then said the fox, 'I will tell thee of yet a greater evil than any I have related heretofore, yea, greater than any of which I have spoken. It was once the custom among the emperors of Rome, that when they hanged a man upon a tree they did not bury him until the tenth day after his hanging. In order that relatives and friends might not snatch the body from the gibbet, an officer of high degree was appointed to keep watch over it through the nights, and if the body were stolen they were used to hang the officer in its stead.

" 'Upon a certain day the emperor caused to be hanged a certain knight who had been rebellious, and the officer was appointed to guard him as was the wont. And it came to pass at midnight that he heard a cry, great and bitter and mighty, a sound of weeping and wailing, and the man was affrighted exceedingly and mounted his steed and said, "I will go and see what this may be, and wherefore." So he rode in the direction of the sound until he came to the burial place of the folk. There he found a woman, embittered of soul, crying in a voice of lamentation, in the dead of night and darkness. He addressed her, "Wherefore, foolish woman, dost thou keen here at midnight, weeping and wailing?" She replied, "My lord, I am a woman of troubled spirit, and therefore do I cry in a voice of lament and weeping, for the Lord hath embittered my soul, for death hath desolated the crown of my head and hath sundered me from mine husband. The covenant, therefore, of weeping and lamentation and mourning and grief shall never depart from me until that I shall return unto dust." But he said to her, "Arise, go to thy house, and there thou mayst keen for thine husband and weep to thine heart's content." He then accompanied her as far as the gates of the city, and thereafter returned to his post.

" 'And it came to pass upon the second night, at a like hour, that he heard again the cry of the woman and her ululation. He ran toward her, and spake gently to her, with lips of loving kindness and mercy. His words were goodly and comforting, and when the woman heard the pleasantness of his words and the softness of his speech, she loved him with all the love of her soul and forgot the sorrow for her husband. She said to him, "My lord, I withhold not from thee thy pleasure, for my soul is bound fast to thine, forged together in the chains of love." So she followed after him and they came to the place of the gibbet and lo, the hanged man had been stolen from upon it.

" 'The officer said to the woman, "Go thee in peace, and I will flee; mayhap I shall escape, for fear of the king troubles my heart sore, lest he find me and hang me upon this tree." She replied to him, "My lord, fear not nor be dismayed, but come rather with me, and we will bring my husband up from the grave, and will hang him instead." But the officer said, "Nay, rather would I choose death and its destruction than casting a man forth from his grave." The woman said, "I shall myself dig down and bring him forth; thou needst incur neither guilt nor sin. Indeed the sage hath said, 'It is permissible to remove the dead from his grave to supply the needs of the living.' " So they returned to the grave and the woman drew forth thence her husband's corpse. But when the officer perceived it he said, "Greatly does it distress me that thou hast dug up this grave, for it avails us naught. The hanged man that was stolen of me was bald, but as for this man, his locks are raven; the thing may not be hidden." But she said, "Quickly will I render his head bald, that no single hair remain." So she plucked out all his hair, and the two lifted him and hanged him upon the tree. And it came about that after a few days the harlot became his wife.'

"When the leopard heard this evil tale, his very bones rattled within him and his heart and his imaginings grew faint, and he went to his house in a great rage and cast fear and trembling upon his wife, saying, 'Get thee from this place as I have bid thee and beguile me not with thy folly, lest I take thy head from upon thee.' The wife saw that evil was determined against her, that the fox had persuaded her lord and caused him to err and that the Satan had come unto him, and that his rage was kindled in him. So she spake softly and said to him, 'Go then to the place thou hast chosen; lo, I follow and do not delay.'

"Thereupon they removed thence, they and their children, and the fox went before them to show them the way and to bring them to that place of infinite goodness. They came to the place and lo, it was a region of great rivers and broad streams, and they encamped there upon the water. The fox gave them his blessing and returned to his house rejoicing from tail to snout, for he saw that his plan had been accomplished. 'The Lord hath now made me at ease,' said he, 'for the leopard is far from my boundaries.'

"After seven days there descended great rains, and all the pits and cisterns and pools were filled, and all the streams were flooded. And it came to pass at midnight, as he and his wife and children were sleeping upon their beds, that the waters prevailed over them and the river overwhelmed them. The leopard sank into the water crying, 'Woe, Woe to him who puts his faith in a fox and his counsel, and doth not hearken to the voice of his wife.' So he perished, dying before his time."

Then Enan Hanatas turned toward me and gnashed his

teeth and sharpened his eyes against me as a sword is ground against an enemy and said: "I marvel at thee. Against whom hast thou uttered this long speech, hast thou lifted thy proverbs, hast thou named me *fox* and thyself *leopard*? Thinkest thou that I am affrighted of thee as was the fox of the leopard? Thinkest thou that I blinded thine eyes when I spake unto thine ears? Truly hath the sage said, 'In the multitude of words there wanteth not sin.' As thy soul liveth, because of thee almost would I despise all my comrades and reject all my friends. Cease then from words of jest and mockery, for they are vanity, deeds of folly. Let us journey forth and go to a land which is not as thy land, wherein thou wilt find all thy delight. Lo, I make a covenant with thee to be thine attendant and minister; in order that I may find favor in thine eyes, I will cause to pass all my goods before thee."

He persuaded me by the strength of his speech and prevailed over me with the smoothness of his lips, for his tongue was as the oil of Aaron that went down to the skirts of his garments. He drew me on with the bonds of his love and with the chains of his kindness and his generosity. So I said to him, "I will but kiss my brethren and my friends, whose love burns in my body, and thereafter will I journey forth with thee."

I kissed all my comrades and wept over them. My heart was moved within me and mine eyes ran streams. After that he had taken me from my native land I went with him in the way that he led me and we journeyed and went upon the king's highway.

Chapter III

Zabara and Enan go upon their way, riding upon their asses. Enan relateth unto Zabara the story of a certain king who dreamed a dream but knew not the interpretation thereof. He sent his eunuch to find an interpreter of dreams. The eunuch met a countryman who had a young daughter that understood dreams. She went with him to the king, explained his dream and became his wife.

And it came to pass after we had gone a furlong, each riding upon his ass, that Enan said to me: "Do thou carry me or I will carry thee; do thou lead me or I will lead thee." I said to him, "But thou art riding upon thine ass and I upon mine: how then may I carry thee or thou me? How can I lead thee or thou me?" "That," he replied, "is the story of the countryman and the king's eunuch." "And what, pray, was that story?" I asked. He said:

"There was once a king, exceeding great both as king and as sage, and he had many wives and concubines. One night he dreamt that he saw an ape of Yemen leap up and spring upon the necks of his wives and concubines. In the morning his spirit troubled him, and his strength was gone from him and he said in his heart, 'Surely this can only be the king of Yemen, who will drive me from my kingdom and lie upon my bed with my wives and my concubines.'

"He arose in the morning, and one of his eunuchs, a personal attendant, came before him, and perceived that he was sorrowful and anxious, that his heart was ill at ease and troubled within him. The eunuch spake, 'Wherefore art thou sad, my lord the king, wherefore hast thou plucked the head of our joy? Reveal thy secret to thy servant, the son of thy handmaiden; perhaps I may avail to remove thy sorrow from thy heart.' The king replied, 'I have dreamed a dream, wherein I have tasted of the bitterness of death. Knowest thou of a man understanding and wise in the interpretation of dreams in these lands?' He replied, 'I have heard that one of the sages, who doth dwell at a distance of three days' journey, is wise and understanding and pure, that he knoweth the meaning of all things, and more, that he can interpret dreams however deep and obscure. Do thou but relate thy dream, and I will go to him.' So the king related his dream and said, 'Go in peace.'

"The eunuch then went down to his house, and mounted his mule and set the interpreter's house as his goal. And it came to pass in the morning that he met a certain countryman who was riding upon an ass. The eunuch hailed him, 'Peace to thee, thou worker of earth, who art thyself earth and yet eat earth.' The countryman laughed at his words. 'Wither goest thou?' asked the eunuch. 'To my house,' the countryman replied. Then the old eunuch said, 'Carry thou me or I will carry thee.' The countryman replied, 'But, my lord, how may I carry thee when thou ridest upon thy mule and I ride upon my beast?' They proceeded another furlong and saw a certain field full of wheat. The countryman said, 'How goodly is this field; surely its sheaves are fitly set.' The eunuch replied, 'If its wheat be not already eaten.' They went yet a little distance more and they saw a tower, lofty and strongly fortified; it was well built and stood upon a rock. The countryman said, 'See this high tower, how comely it is and how well fortified.' The eunuch replied, 'It is indeed fortified without, if it be not destroyed within.' The eunuch remarked, 'There is snow on the height.' The countryman laughed, for it was the month of Tamuz and there was no snow anywhere in the world.

"They went on and came to a road with wheat on the one side and on the other. The eunuch said, 'Upon this road there passed a horse, blind in one eye, and as for his burden, it was oil upon the one side and vinegar upon the other.' They went on and were approaching a city when they saw a corpse being accompanied to its burial. The eunuch asked, 'Is this old man dead or is he alive?' The countryman said in his heart, 'How can this person in his figure seem to be one of the wise, when he is in truth the greatest of fools?'

"When the day was turning to evening the eunuch inquired, 'Is there a place to lodge nearby?' The countryman replied, 'Lo, there is a village before us, where is my house and my place. Do me the honor, prithee, of coming to my house; I have both straw and provender.' The eunuch replied, 'I grant thy request to do as is good in thy sight, and do come into thy house as is thy petition.' So he came into his house and ate and drank and fed his mule, and laid him upon his bed. The countryman laid him down also, and his wife and two daughters were before him.

"And it came to pass at midnight that he roused him from his slumbers and spake to his wife and daughters: 'How great a fool is this man who hath come to our house this night! He met me upon the way, and all the day he wearied me with his words and vexed me with his sayings.' Said his wife, 'What didst thou perceive of his folly?' He told her of the 'carry thou me or I will carry thee,' of the wheat field, the tower, the snow, the road, the corpse, and of his greeting him as one who ate the earth. The countryman's heart waxed bolder as he spake, for he thought that the eunuch lay asleep all the while he was himself wakeful.

"His youngest daughter spoke up and said, being but a lass of fifteen years, 'In truth, father, the man is wise and understanding. 'Tis thou hast failed to attend to him properly. Thou didst not understand the sense of his words, for that his speech was spoken in wisdom and his saying in knowledge and understanding. As for the eunuch's speaking of a worker of earth and eater of earth, he meant to signify that all that man eateth cometh forth from the earth. Thou art thyself truly earth, for dust thou art and to dust returnest. As for "carry thou me or I thee," his meaning was that everyone that goeth upon the way with his neighbor and relateth sayings and stories, and cites puzzles and proverbs, doth thereby carry his neighbor and lead him on, and relieve him of the weariness of the journey and remove him from troubling thoughts. As for the wheat field, he spake truth, for the owner thereof may be poor, and have received the price of the grain in advance, or mayhap he hath borrowed on the security of the grain ere it be harvested. Regarding the tower he also spake truth, for any house which hath not in it grain and bread and viands, that house is destroyed from within and shelters only fear of starvation. When he said, "There is snow upon the height," he meant, "Thy beard is white." Thou shouldst have replied, "Aye, the season hath brought it about." Regarding the horse which was blind in one of his eyes, he may have perceived it from the fact that the grass of the one field was eaten, whereas that of the other was untouched. As for the oil and vinegar, he observed that the vinegar had dried the sand and the oil had not. His question on the corpse was also correct, for if the deceased left a son behind him, he is in truth alive; if not, he is dead.'

"When morning broke the maiden said to her father, 'Ere this stranger depart, do thou set before him what food I give thee.' Thereupon she gave him thirty eggs and a bowl of milk and a whole loaf and said to him, 'Go and inquire of the stranger how many days be wanting of the month, and whether the moon be full, and whether the sun be whole.' The old man went and first ate two of the eggs and a little of the bread, and drank some of the milk; the remainder he gave to the stranger and asked of all the matters which his daughter had bidden. The stranger replied and said, 'Tell thy daughter that the sun is not whole, neither is the moon full, and the month wants two days.' The countryman laughed and said to his daughter, 'Did I not tell thee that this gentleman is simple? For we are at mid-month, and he says but two days are wanting.' 'Father,' said the maid, 'hast thou eaten somewhat of the things I gave thee?' The countryman said, 'I have eaten two of the eggs and a little bread, and I have drunk some of the milk.' 'Now,' said the maid, 'do I know of a surety that the man is truly wise and understanding.'

"When the eunuch heard of the maiden, that her conjectures failed not by the breadth of a hair, he marveled at her wisdom and was amazed. He arose while it was yet morning and delayed not, and said to the father, 'I would have speech with thy daughter, that spoke to thee in the night.' The countryman consented and stood his younger daughter before the stranger. The eunuch spoke with the maiden, and questioned her and examined her, and found her wise and of sound sense in all her speech. He declared his purpose unto her and the matter of the king and his dream. When she heard the account of the dream she said, 'I shall declare the interpretation thereof to the king, if I should see him, but to no man else will I reveal it.' Then the eunuch petitioned the maiden's father and mother to permit her to go with him, for by her going his honor and glory would be increased. He made it known that he was the king's eunuch and intent on the king's business. The countryman feared the king, for that he was his lord, and said, 'Let my lord do as is good in his sight.'

"Then the maiden accompanied him, and he brought her before the king, and related all that had befallen him, and that the maiden would declare the meaning of the king's dream if she but saw him on the throne of his glory. Then the king saw the maiden and she pleased him exceedingly and found grace and favor in his sight. He brought her into a chamber and spoke with her privily and related his dream. She said, 'Fear not, my lord king, all that hath passed in thy dream, for peace is thine and no evil is portended; yet am I abashed from declaring the interpretation, lest I reveal to the king his shame.' He replied, 'Wherefore shouldst thou be ashamed to declare the interpretation of my dream, seeing no man is with me?' She answered, 'My lord king, search among thy wives and maidservants and concubines, and thou wilt find amongst them a man clothed in their habit. He doth come in unto them and lie with them, and he is the ape whom thou sawest leaping upon their necks in thy dream.' So the king searched among his wives and concubines and found among them a handsome youth, comely in form and features, from his shoulder and upwards taller than the crowd; before his countenance gold or silver would be dimmed. The king seized him and butchered him before their eyes and cast his blood in their faces; thereafter he slew them all. And he took the maiden to wife and put the crown royal upon her head, and vowed a vow that never as long as she lived would another woman lie in his bosom, but she alone would be his portion and his lot."

CHAPTER IV

Zabara and Enan come to a village and there lodge. Their food is meager and water is scarce, and also their beasts lack provender. When dawn breaks, they arise and go upon their way.

So we proceeded, Enan and I, and came upon a village and lodged there, for the sun had set. In the lodging house I spake to him and said, "How ravenously hungry am I; give me to eat, for I crave bread and wine." He opened his scrip and placed before me a morsel of his bread and, to the affliction of my soul and the sorrow of my eyes, a bowl full of water. I said to him, "Is this the wont of a friend and neighbor, to serve bread that is dry and moldy?" I cried "Woe!" in a bitter voice for I had tasted naught that day and my soul was grieved and parched; and for the night I had but a dry crust to eat, fit to slay a famished soul.

But he said to me, "Hark! He that is weary from a long journey doth not require abundant victuals, for his members are wearied and his vitals faint, nor have they vigor to digest food that is abundant and rich and heavy, such as meat, whether mutton or beef, or cheese, or all manner of fruit. Indeed King Solomon in his wisdom hath said (Proverbs 17:1): 'Better is a dry morsel and quietness therewith,' but bread can be noxious for no ill or disease." But I said to him, "Good sir, my teacher hath explained that *quietness therewith* signifieth that there should be no strife nor contention." Said he, "Thy teacher was a simpleton and a fool, and knew nothing of the science of food." But I continued, "Woe! and how may I eat a dry crust when my soul is famished by thirst and hunger?" He only laughed at me and said, "Wert thou indeed as famished as thou sayst and were thy soul parched with hunger and faint with thirst, then hadst thou eaten the very dung of the stalls and wouldst not require dainty food, for 'a sated soul despiseth honey.' Eat as I have bidden thee, according as I have instructed thee." But I said in my heart, "May the Lord so be with him as that I shall be satisfied this night with his food."

Alone then did I eat my morsel in the greatness of my hunger, and I was anxious for my sustenance. When I asked for wine to drink he glared at me with an evil eye, and said, "But surely in thine own house thou didst refuse to drink wine and thou didst reproach it and revile it." But I replied to him, "Recall not my words, for now do I require wine to strengthen my limbs." Then said he, "Knowest thou not that a rider is warmed by the motion of his beast, for by motion are limbs warmed, just as they are cooled by rest and quiet? Indeed the philosophers have said, men of wisdom and understanding that they are, that original fire was produced by the motion of the greater orbit, which then became the first basis for all foundations and was the cause and occasion for all creations, from whose union ensued miracles and mysteries. Therefore would I tremble for thee if thou shouldst drink it; nay, water were better for thee far." Then I saw that my speech was futile, that my wine had departed out of the vessel. I took to drinking water till my belly fair burst by the greatness of my thirst.

Of a sudden I heard the braying of mine ass, and on its behalf I bespoke my comrade, "Sir, mine ass is weary, yet hath not provender." He replied, "Give thine ass no provender, lest he perish utterly, for this is the worst of all places, and its provender slayeth all beasts. Therefore do the men of the place not feed it their asses, but give them rather the straw of the wheat." Then said I, "Meseemeth tomorrow will we be reduced to that which thou hast spoken, 'Carry thou me or I will carry thee,' for if the asses eat no fodder this night, they shall in no wise be able to go on the morrow." And since I yet esteemed his person I recited in his hearing these few stanzas: I lifted my parable and said:

> Woe, my belly, my heart, my blood,
> Do thee petition and beg for food.

My bowels cry out, spare good my lord,
Be it but a morsel, let me join thy board.
My limbs complain, sorrow's progeny,
Give me sweet wine, else I die.
Mine ass' plight awakes my tears,
His sorrowful braying racks mine ears.
But hope there is none; mine iniquity dire,
My sin, my guilt, to my doom conspire.
Would some mischance then had refrained me
Ere home I left on baneful journey.

And again:

Mercy, brethren! succor haste,
Spare a fellow creature;
Hunger gnaweth at my entrails:
A morsel, I beseech you!

Then we lay us down upon the ground with neither cushion nor covering. And when dawn brake and the season of departure was nigh, he arose and clothed him in his garments and aroused me and said, "Rouse thee from thy slumber, and let us go forth out of this place, for it is hateful and naughty." But I said to him, "Let me be, for I shall not arise until full daylight, for our sages have said, may their memory be for a blessing, 'Ever should a man enter in with good, and set forth with good,' and *good* signifieth *light*, as it is written (Genesis 1:4). 'And God saw the light that it was *good*.' " But he said unto me, " '*Setting forth with good*' applieth only to ways where danger is to be incurred, but our way is the way of peace and truth, for all the folk of the land are men of kindness and truth." So I arose in the morning, and when I saw the ass before me I recited (Psalms 36:6): "O Lord, thou preservest man and beast!"

Chapter V

Zabara and Enan do pass a certain city, and Enan doth relate to Zabara the wisdom of a certain judge that dwelt there of old.

So we continued upon our journey, and our asses bowed down and knelt as if forsooth they meant to pray. When we approached a certain city my companion fell into great confusion and trembling. When I perceived that he was weeping and that his cheeks were moist with tears, I inquired of him saying, "Wherefore weepest thou, and why do thy tears course down thy cheeks?" He replied, "In this city did my beloved friend and comrade perish; 'tis for him that my tears flow." "What manner of man was he," I asked, "that thou shouldst weep over him?" "A man of wisdom and discernment," he replied, "a man of justice and kindness and faith. He wrought justice ever, in all its forms; nowhere in the world doth any like unto him remain. I will declare to thee a little of his wisdom, and tell thee a moiety of his discernment.

"There came before him once a man, weeping and wailing, and fell upon his face and besought him, 'Give me aid, give me counsel, for overwhelming destruction hath found me.' 'What ails thee that thou criest out,' said he to the man, 'and wherefore do the tears course down thy cheeks?' He replied, 'My lord, I have but one daughter, and for her did I arrange a marriage, giving her to one of the sons of my people. But yesterday I brought unto my house the betrothed lad and his father, and I invited with them my neighbors who are nigh unto me. I showed them her dower of garments and coverings, her mantles and habits, her nose rings and bracelets, her neck chains and pendants: all her ornaments which had been prepared against the day of their wedding, for their gladness and their joy. We arose early in the morning, I and my wife, to cleanse the house and to arrange it, to adorn it and to order it. But we found naught of the garments or ornaments, of the jewels or adornments; there was naught of all her clothing save only her tunic and her slippers. As thine own soul liveth, my lord, that was all my substance and all my wealth, my goods and my possessions, and now I know not what I may do and wherewithal I may dower my clothless daughter.'

"But the wise judge spake to him, 'Lead me to thine house that I may see it; mayhap thou wilt yet discover thy goods.' So he brought him unto his house, and he looked upon the walls of the house, and lo, they were all high, that no thief might ascend the one side and descend to the other, except for one place where there was a breach in the wall, where grew a certain tree of the citrous fruit called *naranja*. The tree is one filled with prickly thorns and the light doth not penetrate it. 'Who is thy neighbor?' inquired the judge. 'My lord,' he answered, 'My neighbor is a precentor, a man just and upright, righteous in all his deeds and words.' The judge turned hither and thither and then went upon his way. 'Return to me at a like hour on the morrow,' said he, 'I shall do for thee that which thou desirest.'

"And it came to pass on the morrow that he sent for the precentor, whose name was Paltiel, the son of Azan. He came then and stood before him, and the judge gazed into his countenance and observed therein indication that the man was not of good faith. The judge then brought him into the chamber and drew off his garments and said to him, 'Do thou draw thy garments off also, and wrestle with me, for last night I saw in my dream that we two were wrangling together being naked, and were wrestling each with the other; and now do I desire to find the interpretation of the dream, wherein may the Lord of peace be our aid.' So the precentor drew off his garments and the judge perceived that his body was filled with sores and bruises and wounds. Just as he had surmised in his heart, so indeed it was; for through that very place had he descended to commit the theft, being naked and without garments, in order that they might not be caught by the thorns which were on the tree.

"Then spake the judge, 'Return that which thou hast stolen, and the dower of thy neighbor's daughter which thou hast taken. If thou refuse, as thy soul liveth, I will scourge thee with rods and with scorpions as a thief and a robber.' Then was the precentor dismayed and affrighted and fell upon his face, nor could he make answer, for that he was confused from before him. And the base evil-doer returned that which he had taken, from a thread even to a shoe latchet. The father returned to the judge as he had been bidden, who then restored to him his daughter's dower. The man fell to the ground full length and kissed his hands and his feet for his kindness and his truth, and said, 'Blessed art thou before God most high, for that thy name is a fortress to the poor and a refuge to the humble.' He took all the goods and returned to his house joyful and glad at heart, and ordered his daughter's marriage as pleased herself and as her heart desired."

Said I, "Lo, I marvel greatly at the decision of the judge and at his wisdom, yea, at the greatness of his knowledge and discernment; yet more do I marvel at the deceitfulness of the precentor and at his devious cunning."

"My son," said my companion, "take thou heed of precentors, for they are mostly robbers; trust not in their words, for they are liars. They seduce women and play the wanton, and share the booty of thieves. They appear friendly, but their mouths are filled with falsehood. They are wise in their own eyes and understanding in their own opinions, though in good truth they know not between their right hand and their left. All the day they read out, but they know not unto whom they read out; they raise their hands aloft, but they understand not unto whom they raise their hands."

I asked of my companion, "Good sir, why do men say that a precentor is ever a fool? Wherefore is he a fool?" He made answer: "When he performeth his office he doth stand higher than all men who are with him, and when he beholdeth himself uplifted and exalted in his office, he doth account it as a mark of his own worth and honor, and doth thereby fall into his folly. Further, when the breath issueth forth from the gullet, it is sundered in the air and giveth birth to voice, whose nature is hot and dry. The voice ever ascends to the brain and withers it, and from the desiccation of the brain arise a man's simplicity and folly. The Lord God, blessed be His name, created the gullet of an intermediary material, which is neither flesh nor bone. For had it been of flesh, it were too soft, and the voice which issued forth from it could not be heard. Similarly, if it were of bone it were too hard, and the voice would likewise not be heard. The breath of the wind is in like case. When it bloweth upon the mighty waters or upon stones that are hard, its voice is not heard; but it is heard when it bloweth upon trees or reeds, for their material is of an intermediary nature, being neither overhard nor oversoft."

"I marvel at thine understanding and thy wisdom," said I, "for no secret is withholden from thee."

Said Enan, "I will tell thee also how that judge by his discernment and clever devices restored to a certain Jew that whereof he had been robbed. There was a certain Jew in Cordova who was called Jacob, the Factor, and he was good and faithful, ready and obedient to the bidding of the judge. One day there was intrusted to him a chain of choice stones and precious pearls to be sold for five hundred pieces of gold. He was walking by the way, carrying the chain in his hand, when he was met by a certain noble of the king's favorites, who thus addressed him: 'Jacob, what manner of chain is that?' He replied to him, 'My lord, it is intrusted to my hand to be sold.' 'And for how much wilt sell it?' 'The price is five hundred pieces of gold,' he replied. Said the noble, 'Wilt sell it for four?' Jacob replied, 'I cannot, for its owner hath laid it upon me not to accept less than five hundred pieces of gold.' The noble said, 'Take it then to my house, and if it please my lady I will buy it.' So he went with him until they reached the gate of his house, where the noble said, 'Stand thou here until

I bring out to thee either the money or the chain.' Thereupon he entered into his house but shut the door behind him; the Jew waited until even, but no man came forth from the door of the house.

"And it came to pass when the sun set, that Jacob went to his house full of wrath; death had been pleasant to him. Sorrow oppressed his heart and wounded it. He came then and lay him upon the ground, nor partook of bread, neither he, nor his sons, nor his wife, nor did his tunic from off him, nor did he close his weary eyes, but tossed all the night, like clay turned to the seal. In the morning he arose and went to the house of the noble, but lo, he had gone forth from his house. He saw him, and ran to meet him, and said to him, 'My lord, buy the chain if thou wilt, or else return it, and I will sell it to another.' The noble replied, 'Of what chain dost thou speak? Hast thou perchance dreamt of a chain?' But he said, 'The chain of pearls which thou didst take from mine hand but yesterday.' 'Thou art lunatic, afflicted with some evil spirit,' said the noble. 'By my life and the life of the king, did I not respect the position I bear, I would take thy head from upon thee, and thyself would I trample in thy heart's blood.' When Jacob perceived his wrath and the hardness of his words, dread of death fell upon him, and he turned his back and fled from before him, for he saw that the noble glared upon him sore.

"He went to the house of his master, the judge, and when the judge looked upon him he perceived that sorrow had bitten into him with its fangs, until that his appearance and the cast of his countenance were altered. The judge addressed him, 'What ails thee that thou hast altered; hast thou then been sorely afflicted?' He replied, 'My lord, I am in sore straits, nor may I tell thee of it, lest thou shouldst discredit my words and distrust my speech.' But the judge said, 'Do thou but relate the matter, for all thy words are faithful in my sight and thou art righteous in all thy speech.'

"So he related all that had befallen in the matter of the

chain and petitioned that his life be spared. Said the judge, 'Remove anger from thy heart and put away sorrow from thine inward parts; tremble not nor groan in thy pain, for I will restore the chain to thee.'

"And it came to pass on the morrow that he summoned all the great men of the city, its elders, and wise men, and sages, to come to the place of judgment, for so was it his wont upon occasion, to send and fetch the wise men and to speak with them of justice. So they all came to his house, to hearken to the words of his understanding and his wisdom. But ere they came the judge said to his servant: 'When that certain noble doth come, take thou his shoe and go to his house and say to his wife, "My lord, thy husband, hath sent me to thee, that thou shouldst give him the chain which he bought yesterday or the day before, for he would display its worth and its beauty, and as a sign and testimony, lo, he hath given me his shoe." '

"When the woman saw her husband's shoe she delivered over the chain, and the servant of the judge brought it to his master and hid it in his bosom until that the men should depart from the seat of judgment. When they had so departed, his master spake to him, 'Hast brought the chain?' 'I have brought it,' he replied, and drew it forth from his bosom, and gave it to him. Then the judge sent and summoned Jacob, the Factor, and said to him, 'Be silent, nor sigh longer, for I have returned thee the chain; I have abstracted from the noble's house that which he hath stolen.' When the Jew saw the chain he kissed the judge's hand and blessed him and carried it to his house joyful and glad at heart.

"I shall tell thee also how he returned an inheritance to the lawful heir, when a slave of the deceased, the son of his maid-servant, had seized it. There was once a merchant, goodly and honored among the merchants and great among the wealthy, and he had but one son. When the lad grew up he said to his father, 'Send me forth and I will go to the countries across the sea, and I will trade, and see diverse lands and regions, and men of instruction, and men of wisdom and discernment, and I will learn of their instruction and discernment, and I will take of their knowledge and wisdom.' The father hearkened to the voice of his son, for this was his only one, and he had abundance of gold and silver. He purchased for him a ship, and gave him great wealth, and sent him forth in peace with certain friends and acquaintances.

"The man was then left alone in his house with his slave, the son of his maidservant, with whom he did deal as he were the apple of his eye, and did hold him in the place of his son, for the servant prospered in all his ways and was diligent in all his needs.

"And after a certain time this man, the master of the house, was seized with a pain in the heart, and his spirit departed from within him, and he died suddenly, nor did he avail to show his thoughts nor to leave his will regarding any matter. So the servant took hold of all that was his, and lorded it over that which his master's labor had acquired, nor was there any man in the city who knew whether he was son or slave, for during his life had the master caused him to have dominion over all his goods and his wealth.

"About ten years, then, after that man's death, his youthful son returned, his vessel being filled with merchandise, all choice goods of every description. But as he was approaching nigh unto his native city, his ship was like to be destroyed. So they cast overboard all their gear and their merchandise which they had acquired, striving to land; but they could not. The youth did reach land, being faint in body and spirit, and he hied him to the house of his parents, that he might cover his nakedness.

"But when the slave found him there he reproached him and reviled him, saying, 'What business hast thou here and whom seekest thou?' And he smote him and cast him forth out of the house and drove him from his heritage.

"The young man went to the judge's house, weeping as he went, and said to him, 'Thus and so hath my slave used me.' He related all that had befallen him, how that he had smitten him and driven him forth from the house, this slave whom his father had made great and exalted. The judge sent to summon the slave, but the youth wept bitter and sore.

"So the slave came before him, and the judge gazed into his eyes, and himseemed the fellow was base, and he spake to him, and said, 'Is it then true that the man whose portion thou hast taken and whose heritage thou hast seized was indeed thy father? For lo, this one declareth that thou art a slave of the household and that no right of inheritance is thine; that thou seekest the right of possession only by willfulness and deceit.' But the slave answered and said, 'My lord, in good truth he was my father and from his loins did I spring; therefore hath he left me all his heritage and his substance, and treasures, and my heart is sore grieved for his sake, for from my youth he nurtured me as a father.'

"But the judge said, 'Produce thy witnesses that thy speech is upright and that thou hast what thou hast in righteousness.' But the slave remonstrated, 'Prithee, let him produce his witnesses, false one that he is, in that he seeks to work deceit with his tears, for upon him who would deprive another who is in possession rests the burden of proof.' So both of them sought witnesses, but could not find them.

"Thereupon they returned to the judge and said to him, 'Our lord, do thou bring our decision forth to the light, for we have no witnesses and to thee do we look for judgment.' Then said the judge, 'Is there a man of you who knoweth the grave of the deceased?' The slave answered, 'I know it, for I myself buried him, as is meet for a son to bury his father.' Thereupon the judge said to his servants, 'Go with him to the grave of this loathly merchant and cast him forth from his sepulcher and bring me his bones, that I may burn them with fire, for that he hath left no will for his household nor declared whose his heritage should be, but did leave behind him quarrels and strife and great and mighty dissension.'

"Then spake the slave, 'I will go according to my lord's bidding and show them the grave, for thou hast uttered true judgment and hast spoken as a very angel of the Lord.'

"But when the son heard the matter of the burning, he cried

out with a soul sore troubled, saying, 'My lord, let the slave take all the heritage of my father, yea, all his glory and all his wealth, but let not my father be cast from his grave.'

"Then said the judge, 'Lo, to thee do I give thy father's heritage and all his wealth and substance, for in truth this fellow is the slave and thou art the son. But as to this slave who hath emboldened his countenance and hath shown no shame, take thou him to be thy slave, and let him serve thee forever.' So the young man went to the house of his parents, taking his bond slave with him, from whom he received wealth and substance and honor."

Then said I to Enan, "In truth thou dost well to weep for him, for he is of the wise men of the age and of its sages."

Chapter VI

Zabara and Enan arrive at a certain city, where an old man doth afford them hospitality, and entertaineth them, and gladdeneth their hearts with diverse stories.

And it came to pass when Enan had done telling of the wisdom of his friend the judge, of his astuteness and discernment and judgments, that we had come upon a road whence we saw a city rising before us, about a furlong away. "Where shall our lodging place be for this night, good sir," said I to him, "and what shall we do for ourselves and our asses?"

But Enan said to me, "Lo this city is nearby, and it is great and spacious, and it enjoyeth a good name, for all its people are righteous and good, kindly folk and gentle."

So we came to the gate of the city, where we were met by an old man of dignified mien, who addressed us saying, "Peace unto ye, my brethren, whence come ye?" "From a far country," we replied, "and for these seven days we have neither stayed nor rested." Thereupon he said unto us, "Come ye then into my house; I shall supply all your wants, for there may ye dine and lodge, both ye and your asses."

So he brought us to his house, and did us honor, and put straw and provender before our asses, saying unto us, "Let it not displease ye that I attend upon these beasts first, for it is worthier to have compassion upon your beasts than upon yourselves, as Solomon of blessed memory hath said (Proverbs 12:10): 'A righteous man regardeth the life of his beast, but the tender mercies of the wicked are cruel. He that taketh pity on his own soul ere he pitieth his beast is both wicked and cruel.' "

Then he bade us wash our feet, but we said, "Wherefore have we thus found grace in the eyes of our lord, that he should favor us with all these many kindnesses?" But he said unto us, "Hesitate not, but wash your feet; for he that cometh from the way requireth to wash his feet, for washing of the feet is salutary for aches of the head and the eyes, and doth cause weariness to depart, and sharpeneth the appetite that one may take pleasure in his victuals, and hasteneth restful slumber."

So the servant washed our feet, and put viands before us, and we ate and drank with him. And in the course of the drinking he gladdened our hearts with good words and with sayings sweet and pleasant, and also with a story exceeding marvelous:

"In the days of the saints of old and the sages of an elder day there dwelt in this city a man upright and righteous and straightforward in all his speech. The man was great and wealthy, and his eyelids looked straight before him. His name was Tobias, son of Ahijah, the Danite. It was his wont to give food and lodging to every poor and needy person. If any died without relatives to bury him, he prepared shrouds out of his own purse, and wrought what was necessary, and buried him.

"But the people of this city were exceedingly evil, being willful and faithless, and they slandered all the Jews before the king, saying, 'Lord King, these Jews do open our graves, and draw thence the bones of our dead, and burn them daily to make magic remedies.' The wrath of the king was kindled when he heard these words, and he commanded that the yoke of the Jews and their bonds be made heavier. 'Let this,' said he, 'be their reward: Any Jew that shall die in all my kingdom, let him be cast into a great pit which is near the city, and let anyone that doth bury him be hanged upon a tree.'

"Came a day when a certain proselyte died, and there were none to bury him. Then arose saintly Tobias and washed him, and clothed him, and buried him. But wicked people had seen him, and they seized him and brought him to the judge and said to him, 'Sir judge, this Jew hath transgressed the ordinance of the king; he hath buried one of the sons of his people.' So the judge bade that he be hanged, for that he had transgressed upon the king's ordinance and his statute. So they took him without the city to hang him upon the tree which they had prepared for him.

"But when they had come near the tree, lo! they were smitten with blindness from great to small, and could not see him. Then Tobias escaped from them, and returned to his home and invited his loved ones and his relatives and his companions and all that had mourned for his affliction, and he related to them all that had befallen him and the mercy which the Lord had vouchsafed him, and he said unto them (Psalms 106:1) 'Praise ye the Lord for He is good, for His mercy endureth forever. There is no god, no providence, beside Him; praised be the name of His glory, for that He delighteth in the peace of His servant.'

"And it came to pass when the king came unto the city, that they related unto him all that had befallen them with the Jew, when they had sought to hang him. The king trembled exceedingly and his heart smote him within him, and he commanded that the order be proclaimed throughout his kingdom, that anyone who wrought hurt to a Jew, whether in his person or in his substance, did in effect injure the apple of his own eye. Every man that harmed them should be hanged upon a tree, even if his person were respected and he were himself a counselor. And he commanded that the Jews bury their dead in honor, and he uplifted them and exalted them all the days of his life. But those wicked men nevermore saw the light all their days.

"One day that saintly man was lying upon his bed, and there was a swallow's nest in his house. When he opened his eye to look at the nest there fell into his eyes of the swallow's dung, so that they were dimmed from seeing, for a film of white had covered his eyeball. He had but one son, only child to him and to his mother, and him he called and spake to him and said:

" 'Son, when I was engaged in the business of commerce, I

wandered about all lands and traveled in all countries. One day I went to the land of Ind and traded there until that I had accumulated much wealth by my earnings. But because of the terror of the roads I intrusted my riches into the hand of a good and faithful man, whose name was Pride of the Age. And now, my son, hearken to my voice and go and hire me a man of them that travel upon the ways, one that knoweth the paths of the land of Ind. And I will send thee with him to that faithful man to whom I committed my silver and gold. I know that when he shall behold thee, my son, and the sign of the writing which is between him and between me, that he will give thee my wealth; for he is a faithful man and doth love me, and will have pity upon me when he shall hear of my disease and my pain.'

"So the lad went to the place of the hirelings and found there a certain man who knew all the land of Ind and its paths, the whole country and its diverse places. Him he brought to his father and said, 'Lo I have found this man, who knoweth all the land of Ind and its ways, even as he knoweth this city and its avenues.'

"Pious Tobias inquired of him, 'Dost know a certain city in the land of Ind whose name is Tobat?' 'Worthy sir,' he replied, 'I do indeed know it, for I dwelt therein two full years; it is a great city for sages.' Said Tobias, 'What shall I give thee, that thou shouldst go thither with my son?' 'Fifty pieces of gold,' he replied. The saintly one said, 'I will give them thee with joy and with gladness of heart.'

"So he wrote the script to the man of good faith, and made therein the sign, and took his son and embraced him, and fell upon his neck and kissed him, and said to him, 'Go in peace, and may the God of my fathers keep me alive until thou return hither.'

"So the lad went with the man that was hired until they came to the city of Tobat. There this man brought him to the faithful one whose name was Pride of the Age. To him the lad spake, 'My Lord, art thou the faithful man whose name is

Pride of the Age?' The other replied, 'Wherefore dost thou inquire after my name?' 'My father Tobias, the Danite, has sent me to thee,' said the lad, 'and lo, he seeks thy peace and the peace of all that are thine'; thereupon he gave him the writing of his father.

"When the man beheld the script and its sign, he cast his eye over it and believed the lad was in truth Tobias' son, and embraced him and kissed him and sustained him with honey and milk, and said to him: 'Doth my friend and comrade, my bosom companion and beloved one, enjoy peace?' 'He doth so,' was the reply. Then the man rejoiced in his friend's son and messenger, and the nard of his love was fragrant. 'Abide with me yet a month,' said he, 'and I will rejoice in thee and in thy pleasant speech.' But the lad said to him, 'My lord, send me forth, and let me go to my place and my country, for such is the will of my father and mine own will and pleasure, for from that day that I forsook my elderly father my heart hath trembled and hath been disturbed, for my father hath no son beside me, and therefore do I hasten, with the help of our Rock, to return to my home.' Then did the faithful one fulfill his every wish, and deliver up unto him all his father's substance and his wealth, and added yet gifts of his own and garments and diverse other things; two serving lads also did he give him to attend him, and he sent him away with songs and rejoicing.

"And it came to pass on the way, as they were going by the shore of the sea, that its waves were roused by a strong and mighty wind, and cast up a fish before them upon the dry land. The hireling hastened to seize it, and when he had opened its belly he took forth its liver and gall. The lad addressed him: 'As thy soul liveth, wherefore hast thou left the fish behind and taken only its liver and gall?' He replied, 'Know that in these two things lieth great salvation, for of them potent remedies may be made. Into no house in which this liver is burned as incense will ever destroying demon come; never will its masters be endangered, ever will they be at peace. And for the gall, if a blind man should paint his eyes therewith they would be opened, and his eyeballs would become bright.' Thereupon the lad besought his companion earnestly that he give him the organs, and he took them and bound them in the skirts of his garment.

"So the lad arrived at his home rejoicing and found his father safe and secure. Then did the man rejoice over his son, and moreover over his substance and his riches, and he said unto his son, 'Go with this hireling unto the banker and give him an hundred pieces of gold, yea more, an he will, and return payment to him as him pleaseth.'

"So the lad went with the man, and gazed after him but beheld him not, and sought him in all the city but could not find him. Then he came to his father and said, 'I did go with the man, but when I gazed after him I beheld him not, and though I sought him in all the city I could not find him.' Thereupon his father declared unto him, 'Son, know thou that our God hath sent him before us to preserve us alive; in truth he is the prophet Elijah.'

"Then the lad related the matter of the liver and gall and gave them to his father, who then painted his eyeballs with the gall, which the Lord then opened, and restored unto them their sight.

"Thereafter the man spake unto his son: 'My son, after that the Lord hath led thee in the path of truth, nor hath spared His eye from watching over thee, but hath delivered thee from all mishap and evil, and hath hearkened to our voice and returned thee unto us in peace — do thou therefore hearken unto my voice and perform a great kindness and a worthy deed. Take thou to wife the lass that is my brother's daughter, for she doth see that all her companions be wedded and is herself covered with shame.'

"Now regarding this maiden there was a great portent and marvelous, for thrice had she been wedded to men; but by reason of this great portent everyone that lay with her was thereafter found dead, lying prone on his couch. So the lad replied, 'Father mine, how may I come nigh unto her? I do indeed dread lest I die by reason of her, for already have her three husbands perished.'

"But he said to him, 'My son, know of a truth that it is some demon or destroying angel that doth slay them and take from them their souls. Do thou but take the liver which the man hath given thee, and burn it as incense in the house as he hath directed; then trust in the Lord, and thou wilt be warded from all evil.'

"So the lad took his life in his hand and stiffened not his neck from doing his father's bidding, and he took the maiden, and she became his wife and he did love her.

"And it came to pass at even, that he burned the fish's liver as incense throughout the house, from without and within, and his bed also, and his covering and his garments, and the maiden came unto the chamber, and he came in unto her. But his elderly and saintly father wept and prayed before the Lord, and his heart trembled and sighed within him for the fate of his son. But the young man lay until the light of morning, and when they rose early to seek his peace, they found him rejoicing and glad at heart, free from any disease or sorrow. And the two lived on without fright or fear and ended their days in goodness and their years in pleasantness."

Another story also did this hospitable old man tell us:

"In olden days there was in this city a certain man righteous in all his ways and saintly in all his deeds. His house lay upon the road to the burial ground, and of all who died the bier was wont to pass before the door of his house; then would the man attend the corpse to the burial place and give aid to them that buried it. But at the season of his old age he fell to his bed, for he was diseased with a pain in his legs, until that his thighs were wholly unavailing, so that he could not support himself upon them nor could he stand upright.

"Upon a day there died in the city a certain saintly man who loved peace and pursued righteousness and repaired the fortune of all, as far as in him lay. When his corpse passed the door, and the old man found he could not rise from his bed to accompany it, his sorrow oppressed him sore. He forgot his disease and his pain, and cried to the Lord all the night, saying: 'Lord, God of heaven, Thou who hast given eyes to the blind and to the lame feet, after that Thou has afflicted me with this disease of my feet, do Thou answer me from my couch of pain; hearken to my prayer and fulfill my petition! Whensoever the corpse of a saintly or righteous man doth pass by my house door, do Thou make me firm and strong, so that I may rise to my feet.'

"Then did the angel of the Lord make answer to him in a vision, 'Lo, I have granted thy petition for this thing.' And now, whensoever any righteous dead would pass the door of his house, he would rise upon his bed and pray for the departed soul.

"One day there died in the city an old man of dignified mien, the crown of eld, goodly in the sight of God and men; but when the corpse passed his house the old man could not rise from before him. It happened on the morrow that a certain butcher died, a man of strife and contentions, filled with transgression and rebellious, hard and of evil deeds, and exercised in every manner of sin and iniquity; yet when his bier passed before the saintly old man, he arose to his feet and stood erect.

"Then did all that beheld remark in amazement, 'Can it then be that this butcher is not of the sinful?' And the people marveled, each man to his neighbor, and said, 'How came it that the pious man arose this day from before the butcher, but yesterday he arose not from before the elder, nor did he stand?' And all the people of the city heard and marveled and said, 'It signifieth somewhat.'

"Then did two elders arise, men of righteousness, warders of the faithful, and declared, 'We shall not rest until that we have seen what this great thing may be.' So they went to the wife of the butcher and questioned her regarding her husband. But she put upon them with her voice and said unto them,

'Make no mention of that wicked man, for he was a transgressor even from his mother's womb. All the day would he smite me though I sinned not, and was overweening, and bore himself as if to slay me. And he would glower with his eyes and gnash his teeth, and he slew his own sons, and awoke strife all the day, and all but desolated his own house; in short he was naughty and hard-hearted and contemned all the Laws of Moses.

" 'But one good quality was found in him, for he had an aged father, a hundred years old, to whom he rendered honor and service. Every day did he kiss his hand, and give him to eat and to drink, and drew off his clothing, and drew it on again, for because of his great age he availed not to turn himself upon his bed. Each day would he bring him the bones of kine and sheep and would break them and draw their marrow from them, and make him pottage; thus ever was his wont toward his father.' Then did they know that the honor he bestowed upon his father had worked remission for his sins and pardon for his iniquities, and he went to his eternal rest pure and innocent of all sin and guilt.

"Thereafter they went to the house of the elder and questioned his wife regarding her husband. With a sorrowing soul did she answer them: 'My husband, may he rest in peace, from that day whereon he wedded me, hath neither rebuked me nor made me ashamed. He made me mistress over all that he possessed. Never did he smite me, nor any of his slaves nor sons; his heart was not haughty nor his eyes proud. Thrice daily did he let fall his supplication before God, awful and exalted, and at midnight would he rise from his couch and enter into a chamber to pray and to do obeisance before his Creator.'

"They then asked of her, 'Where is that chamber wherein he was used to pray?' So she showed it them, but it was locked. 'As my soul liveth, and by mine husband's honor,' quoth she, 'these twenty years have I not entered it, nor hath any of my sons. To no man was it open, for himself did carry the key in his bosom.' Then the elders opened the chamber, and found naught therein save only a little chest, hidden away in an opening. This they opened and found therein an image of gold in the likeness of a man, and in his hand was a crucifix.

"Then they knew that to him had the elder prayed morning and evening, and they knew that he was a wicked heretic and had violated the eternal covenant, in that he ate of the bread of man and drank the wine of the condemned. He stole the hearts of men, as did the heretics of Shechem who did as their namesake had done (Genesis 34), in that they circumcised their flesh not for the glory of the Creator, but to satisfy their love; or like a heretic of the Smitten also, who woundeth his own feet and declareth unto men, 'I cannot stand, for that I have journeyed to a distant land for to buy sacramental objects or to the feast of a circumcision or a marriage'; or as the heretic of the Calculators or the Pestle heretics, and other heretics also, who separate their hearts from the good, and cleave rather to the evil. May He who exacted punishment of the men of the generation of the Deluge speedily exact punishment from them also, and from those that are falsely painted to resemble the faithful, who cover their heads in prayer and display their prayer shawls and their fringes, who pronounce the words of their prayer unctuously. May the Lord have no mercy upon them nor pity them, for they do the deeds of Zimri and seek the reward of Phineas.* Of them hath the bard sung:

> These are the men in their own sight wise,
> Others naught are counted in their eyes.
> In their hearts hath nested pride,
> But their souls are all untried;
> Their bellies stuffed by deceit and guile
> As leathern bottle filled with oil.
> On their lips peace, but in their hearts
> Armor and swords and warlike darts.

* These heresies are all described in a passage in the Babylonian Talmud, Sotah 22 b.

In unctuous prayer lies all their piety,
Of works of charity never a moiety.
My life, O Lord, till that hour spare
When I as Cain and they as Abel fare.

"These are the folk that display uprightness and humility, appearing to be righteous and saintly, whereas they are in truth transgressors and rebellious. They are like a mirror which doth show to them that look therein objects which it containeth not. The nature of them all is as that of the black choler which seeth evil images and monsters in the night, such as demons and evil spirits, nightmares and similitudes of things that are not."

And it came to pass when the good man, full of days and hoary, had made an end of narrating his pleasant words unto us, that we lay us down upon our beds, and our sleep was sweet unto us for that we had eaten of fatted calves. We did not awaken until we were roused by the light of day, then did we saddle our asses, and we embraced our good host and kissed him and blessed him and praised him for his generosity and his kindness.

Chapter VII

Zabara and Enan come to a certain city where dwells Rabbi Judah, an intimate of Enan; he doth hospitably invite them into his house, and arrayeth a table before them, and maketh their hearts glad with pleasant parables.

So we went forth and journeyed from his house, and my comrade Enan led me through by roads and side paths and ways that were crooked, of which I had neither heard nor known. And it came to pass at even that I saw before me a certain city; my heart had sunk low with hunger and with thirst. Being filled with wonder and amazement, I spake to Enan: "What manner of city is this that I behold before me?" He replied unto me, "The city is well situated and pleasant, and holdeth nine friends and comrades, of which one is called Rabbi Judah; his house will be our lodging this night, and there will we eat and drink as shall please us." So we came unto the city, and he brought me to the house of a certain hoary sage, goodly among the elders, wise and understanding; this man received us with joy and gladness, and welcomed us with honor and peace, saying, "Now do I know of a surety that pleasantness is come, for my dear friend is come unto my house, my neighbor, my comrade, my confidant." And he bade us wash our feet, and put straw and provender before our asses. Then did he slaughter his meat and mingle his wine; he arrayed his board and put viands before us, and all manner of spices.

And when we had eaten and were satisfied, and had delivered grace and benediction to the Lord, he prepared for us a sumptuous beverage, compounded of grapes and the juice of pomegranates. That our hearts might be of good cheer the elder said: "Would it please you to hearken to words of pleasantness that I have gleaned from the books of the Arabs?

They are pleasant and goodly, and ye will find delight in them as ye find delight in choice viands." We made answer to him: "Good sir, after thou hast afforded us pleasure with these, thy delicious victuals, let us hearken also to thy pleasant words." So he spake:

1. "A man once said to a sage, 'Thou lordest it over us with thy wisdom; but in truth in the beginning it came from us.' 'Right,' said the Sage, 'from you hath it come, but it hath never returned unto you.'

2. "A man once reproached another, who then made no reply. They said to him, 'Wherefore makest no reply?' He answered, 'I will enter no quarrel where the victor suffers defeat.'

3. "An angry man once said to his son, 'Hush, thou harlot's son!' The son said in reply, 'Only a child of harlotry would lie with a harlot.'

4. "One of the wise men praised the king, who did then suspect him. Said he, 'I am the more suspect because thou suspectest me than thou art wise because I have praised thee.'

5. "They asked a sage, 'Who of the sons of men is evil?' 'He that thinketh he is good,' he replied.

6. "They asked a sage, 'What is clarity?' He replied, 'To speak without erring, and to be brief without repeating.'

7. "A certain king said to one of his sages, 'How pleasant it were if kingship but lasted forever!' He replied, 'If it were so, thou hadst never been king.'

8. "A certain one cried out to the king, 'My lord, thine officer hath robbed me!' But the king only reviled him. The man said, 'I entered with one plaint, and now I depart with two.'

9. "Two men came before a judge to be adjudged, the one being hoary and the other but a youth. The judge said, 'Shall we respect great age?' The youth replied, 'But truth is greater.' 'Be silent!' said the judge. 'Then who will plead my cause?' asked the youth. 'Meseemeth,' said the judge, 'that in thy mouth there is no word of truth.' Said the youth, 'The

Lord is one and His name one!' The judge arose and went to the king's house as was his wont, and reported the speech of the youth. The king said, 'Grant his petition but cause him to depart hence, lest he corrupt our kingdom.'

10. "One day the king came to the house of one of his nobles and asked of the noble's son, who was but a small lad, 'Whose house is better, mine or thy father's?' 'My father's house is better as long as the king is therein, answered the little lad.'

11. "The king once clothed him in a new garment, but it was not seemly. Quoth he, 'This new garment is not good for to clothe oneself.' 'If not,' said one of his servants, 'it is good for to clothe another'; so the king drew it off and gave it him.

12. "A bard was once reciting his songs before a gathering of his companions and friends, among whom was a young lad. Of him he asked, 'Are my songs pleasant in thine eyes and my words sweet?' 'Yea verily,' quoth the lad. 'Wouldst then rejoice if I were thy father?' 'Nay, but I would gladly have thee my mother, that my father might enjoy thy embraces,' answered the lad; and the poet was put to shame.

13. "A certain one came before a judge and complained. Asked the judge, 'Against whom bringest thou complaint?' The man answered, 'Against thine own agent, for he hath stolen my field and joined it to thine.' Said the judge, 'Thou hast need of witnesses and testifiers and other matters.' The man replied, 'The witnesses are the testifiers; they and the other matters proceed from thee.' The judge fell silent and bade his agent return the field.

14. "A certain dullard went to visit a sick man, and asked, 'Dost recognize me?' The sick replied, 'And who would not recognize thine ill favor and thy folly?'

15. "Another dullard visited a sick man to comfort him of his disease, and said, 'What evil hath befallen thee by reason of thy disease?' He replied, 'That thou hast come to visit me.'

16. "They asked a sage, 'What is the thing of which all men have need?' 'Good fortune,' he replied.

17. "A man of gentle birth reviled a sage for that he was of humble birth. He replied, 'My birth is a disgrace to me, but thou art a disgrace to thy birth.'

18. "Another also reviled him for his birth. He replied, 'My family distinction begins with myself, thine ends with thee.'

19. "Once this sage, whose name was Diogenes, went abroad with a wealthy man to go to a certain place, and on the way they saw robbers approaching. The wealthy man said, 'Woe is me if they recognize me'; but Diogenes said, 'Woe is me if they recognize me not.'

20. "They asked a sage, 'What is the thing which behooveth not to be said even if it be true?' He replied, 'That a man praise himself.'

21. "They asked a sage, 'When is a little wisdom better than much?' 'When the wisdom is excessive for a brain that is puny.'

22. "When a certain philosopher saw a man shooting arrows which went to the right and to the left, he went and sat him at the place of the target. They asked, 'Why dost sit in the place of danger?' Quoth he, 'I behold no place safer.'

23. "When Diogenes beheld a man handsome in form and figure but prone to lie he said, 'The house is comely, but its dweller ill-favored.'

24. "Again, when a certain wicked lad, whose mother was a harlot, was casting stones, Diogenes said to him, 'Forbear, lest thou smite thy father.'

25. "When they asked him concerning death he replied, 'Death is fearful to the wealthy, but to the poor a delight.'

26. "They asked a certain pious man, 'What sayest thou in thine even prayer?' He replied, 'He that feareth God by day sleepeth sound by night.'

27. "When the brother of a certain Arab died, they asked, 'What occasioned his death?' 'His life,' was the reply.

28. "Of an Arab pauper was asked, 'What hast thou set by for the winter?' 'A cold,' he replied.

29. "One called his father's wife, 'Harlot.' 'Were I a

harlot,' she replied, 'I would have borne thy father such a son as thou art.'

30. "One said to his wife, 'Had I my good way I would slay thee.' 'Wherefore?' she asked. 'Because thou art a harlot.' 'Wouldst then slay all harlots?' she asked. 'Aye,' he replied. 'Begin with thy mother then,' quoth she, 'and end with thy wife.'

31. "A man entered a House of Prayer and saw there a man, passing ill-favored, praying his God that he be delivered from Gehenna. He approached him and said, 'I will give thee good counsel.' 'And what may it be?' the man asked. 'Do but show thy countenance only to those in Gehenna.'

32. "When a sage beheld a fool sitting upon a stone he said, 'Lo, stone upon stone.'

33. "They asked the philosopher Socrates, 'Wherewith may a man avenge himself of his enemies?' 'By increasing his own might and fame,' he replied.

34. "When is silence better than speech? At the time of lustfulness.

35. "They asked of Plato, 'Wherefore are not wisdom and wealth combined in one body?' 'Because they are contraries,' he replied.

36. "The sage hath said, 'Man's superiority over all creatures lieth in speech and wisdom; if he be silent and wanting in understanding he is like unto a beast.'

37. "They said to a certain sage, 'The king loveth thee not.' 'Then,' quoth he, 'the king loveth not one who is greater than he.'

38. "When he was asked, 'Which is the most beautiful of the beasts?' he replied, 'Woman.'

39. "An enemy that is wise is better than a foolish friend.

40. "Better that a gentle noble die, than that a knave be exalted.

41. "Prosperity is comprised in three things, that thou shouldst abide in thine house, and keep thy tongue, and weep for thine iniquity.

42. "Hide thy righteousness even as thou hidest thy sins.

43. "Not all that flee escape, nor are all in need who beg.

44. "One of the sages hath said, 'I marvel that a man's sleep is pleasant, seeing that the angel of death lieth upon his bed.'

45. "A man made proclamation, 'Who of the kings would buy three things of me for twelve thousand denarii?' They that heard him marveled, and the matter reached the ears of the king. The king commanded that he be brought, and when he came he questioned him concerning those three things. 'First get thy wealth ready,' said the man, and the king commanded that it be got ready. Then he spake: 'The first thing is, there is none good among thy sons; second, it behooveth thou shouldst know thou mayst not stand without them; third, it behooveth thou shouldst deal with them according to their character.' When the money was given him he said, 'I require it not; I but wished to know whether there remained of those who seek wisdom or not.'

46. "A certain son of the sages was made captive, and when they brought him out to be sold they asked of him, 'What knowest thou?' 'That I am not a freeman,' he replied; so they loosed him.

47. "A sage, the light of whose eyes had failed, was asked, 'Wherefore healest thou not thine eyes?' He replied, 'Whom should I look upon?'

48. "A certain man contended with a sage and said, 'If thou sayest one thing I will say ten.' 'If thou shouldst say ten,' quoth the sage, 'thou wouldst not understand even one.'

49. "A certain king sat upon his throne and dispensed justice to his people. A dwarf came before him and cried out: 'Lord king, hear the plaint of him that is oppressed!' but the king paid him no heed. Then said one of his ministers to the king, 'Wherefore hearkenest not to the cry of the oppressed?' Said the king, 'No man would oppress such a dwarf as he.' 'But Lord king,' said the dwarf, 'he that oppresseth me is even smaller than I.' So the king laughed and heard his cause.

50. "One of the bards met a certain noble whom he had reviled in his poems, and asked for pardon. Said the noble, 'With what face dost thou address me now, seeing thou hast reviled me in thy poems?' The poet answered, 'With the same face that I address my Creator, praised be He, when I ask pardon for my many transgressions and iniquities.'

51. "A king overheard a certain woman crying, 'Merciful Ruler, remove this king from over us!' He said, 'Add to thy prayer, "And change him for one that is better than he."'

52. "Prepare for this world as thou shouldst live forever.

53. "Prepare for the world to come as thou shouldst die tomorrow.

54. "The faithful man will not be found, nor will the thief be missed.

55. "A certain sage gave comfort to a mourner by saying: 'All that the Creator hath created is small at first and afterwards waxeth great; except mourning, for it is great at first and afterwards waneth until it disappears.'

56. "The agent revealeth the mind of him that sent him.

57. "A youth saw an elder walking with difficulty, and said, 'Who hath enchained thy feet?' Quoth he, 'Time, which I leave behind me, will make a chain for thy feet also.'

58. "A philosopher was asked, 'What is a good shelter for a man?' 'The grave,' he replied.

59. "He that clotheth himself in broidered garments, being bare of wit and wisdom, is like unto a peacock, which, when his feathers are removed, resembleth a plucked cock.

60. "In thy reliance on balm, eat not poison.

61. "A wise man is a universe.

62. "A certain one of the philosophers fell sick of a grave disease, so that his physician despaired of his being healed; but afterwards he did in fact become well. When the physician met him in the street he said to him, 'Thou comest from the other world.' 'Aye,' said the philosopher, 'I do indeed come thence, and there I saw that many and great afflictions are put upon physicians, for that they slay men. But be thou cheerful and of good courage, for thou are not of their number, for so

I swore regarding thee, that thou art neither physician nor know aught of the healing art.'

63. "A certain noble sent a kid to the king, saying, 'Eat of its kidneys, for they do enlarge the brain.' Said the king, 'If it were indeed so, a king's head had been as the head of a mule.'

64. "Two lunatics were summoned before the king, to be made sport of, but they angered the king with their words and incensed him with their folly, so the king summoned the executioner. They said, 'Woe betide us! We came being two and now we return three.' So the king laughed, and slew them not.

65. "A certain one asked, 'Where are the pious of this world who do seek the other world?' A sage made answer, 'Turn thy words about, then mayst thou seize upon whomsoever thou wilt.'

66. "His disciples petitioned a certain sage, 'Teach us what thou hast learnt of the Creator, praised be He.' Quoth he, 'When ye practice what ye have learnt, I will teach you what ye know not.'

67. "A man who was wont to come to a certain noble's house riding upon his ass, came one day on foot, whereupon the noble said, 'What hast befallen thy beast?' 'My lord,' he replied, 'provender is very dear, and I could not keep it.' 'Didst think,' was the reply, 'I would give thee its keep?'

68. "A certain man called upon the king by name, whereupon the king said, 'Woe betide thee, how callest thou me by name?' The man replied, 'The Creator, be He praised, is called upon by His name; and wilt not thou be called by thine?'

69. "One of the philosophers who did instruct was asked, 'And who doth give thee instruction?' 'I observe the fool,' he replied, 'and do the opposite; and thus am I instructed.'

70. "Love improveth relationship, and relationship is the highest gentility.

71. "Love is a tree and visiting is the fruit thereof, of which less is better than much.

72. "Three things do weary a man, which are: a lamp

whose light is dark; a messenger that tarryeth, and a table that awaiteth one who is to come.

73. "In three ways is man known: by his dealing with his fellow men, by his quickness in granting pardon, and by his love of his fellow men.

74. "By three things is a fool recognized: by his quickness in answering, his volubility, and his faith in all men.

75. "One asked of a sage, 'Advisest thou that I learn the ascetic life? It is highly respected.' The sage replied, 'Thy life is thine own; spend it as thou wilt.'

76. "They said to a certain Nazarite, 'Wherefore is thy dress black?' He replied, 'Because it is more seemly for the iniquitous.'

77. "They asked a Nazarite, 'How appeareth time?' He replied, 'It withereth bodies and reneweth cares.'

78. "When is mourning good? When the fool hath died and the wise surviveth.

79. "A man need but be perfect in three things, which are knowledge and wisdom and religion; and natural science hath naught better than these three; for knowledge is the body's ruler, and wisdom doth guide it, and religion is its lamp and light.

80. "Lions for strength, oxen for burden, spiders for weaving, bees for building, and ants for storing treasures.

81. "Dread time, even when it smileth on thee.

82. "Man is forgetful of good when it is present; but when it hath gone, he knoweth it.

83. "A sage was asked, 'What doth it behoove a man to beware of?' He replied, 'The envy of brethren and the might of enemies.'

84. "Socrates hath said: 'Constancy of thought attaineth to counsel, refraining from anger maketh the soul to rest, taciturnity increaseth reverence, upright speech provoketh love, by loving kindness is quality exalted, in humility goodness taketh its stand, perseverance bringeth about prosperity, humility causeth its own assistance, evil conduct indicateth a base root, and covetousness minisheth every man's calm.'

85. "How often doth a man take pleasure in a good which is really an evil, and envy a lot which would afford him only discomfort!

86. "Sorrow is partial dissolution; poverty death itself.

87. "Lying is justifiable in only three instances: in war, for then it is cunning strategy; in making peace between man and his neighbor; and when a man giveth pleasure to his wife.

88. "They asked a sage, 'Which is a good and honored comrade?' He replied, 'One that hath good works and reverence.'

89. "Who is wicked and despised? A covetous spirit.

90. "My lord hath commanded me; so have I done.

91. "Who is the gentlest of men? He who sacrificeth this world for the sake of the world to come.

92. "Who is mighty among men? He who feareth the Lord with all his heart.

93. "A philosopher beheld a certain man whose father had bequeathed great wealth unto him, which he had then wasted and lost, eating of bread and salt olives. Said he to him, 'Hadst thou thought this were thy fare, this had not been thy fare.'

94. "Aristotle was asked, 'What is the body of man?' 'A thing prepared to receive bruises and accidents,' he replied.

95. "Man is a son of his age.

96. "One asked of a philosopher, 'Wherefore is sea water salt?' 'If thou wilt tell me how it will profit thee,' he replied, 'I will tell thee the cause.'

97. "An officer vowed to an acquaintance that he would give him a mule and its fittings, which the acquaintance one day claimed. The officer said, 'As thy soul liveth, I will not withhold from giving it thee, if thou but withhold not from seeing me.' He replied, 'Give me this and vow another; then will I not withhold from seeing thee.'

98. "A man laid upon his son: 'When thou takest a wife, take neither one who is overmerciful, nor overmournful, nor prone to refuse; not overmerciful, lest she take pity upon her son of an earlier marriage; nor mournful, lest whenever she

see thee she make mourn for her first husband and say, 'Lord pity his soul'; nor prone to refuse, lest she refuse to give or lend thee of the wealth she possesseth.

99. "A certain king had a ring whereon was graven, 'Thou hast become tedious; go!' Whenever anyone overstayed his welcome he would show him the ring, and he would depart."

When he had made an end of uttering his beauteous words and pleasant speeches, we laid us upon our couches and our sleep was sweet to us. And when morning came we took leave of him, and thanked him for his goodness and his kindness, and departed from him in peace.

Chapter VIII

Enan doth bring Zabara unto his city and his house, and his servant arrayeth a table before them, whereon he placeth unleavened bread, and lettuce, and a bowl of vinegar. At these meager viands Zabara murmureth, whereupon Enan doth bid his servant bring flesh. While the servant prepareth the victuals they do dispute regarding good health, and Enan doth adduce proofs from the sayings of the ancient philosophers that it behooveth a man to beware of excess in eating. Finally the slave bringeth the meat, but Enan permitteth Zabara to eat naught save only the bones, and doth argue that the remaining members of the sheep be not fit for food. Zabara refuseth to hearken unto his voice, and doth eat until that he is satisfied.

Then did my comrade Enan lead me yet farther, by a path unknown even to the crows and by a river navigated by no vessels, and towards evening I beheld a city surrounded by strong walls, with entrance fortified. Before the city was an orchard, in which bloomed all manner of fruit trees, and which was redolent of diverse spices. Then said I unto him, "Prithee, what city is this?" He replied, "This is the city which I have chosen, herein it is my delight to dwell, herein is my place and my home, my rest all the days of my life." So we came thither, and he did bring me to his house, and showed me his dwelling. But I spake to him, "Good sir, eating and drinking are more wholesome for the body than seeing." But he said, "Be not overhasty in thy speech, for ofttimes he that hasteth overmuch must needs be delayed." Then did I, Joseph, say in my heart, "Now will he do with me what him pleaseth; therefore hath he brought me unto his place and his country; now do I know that he plotteth against me, for ever did he contend with me over victuals, and now I fear lest he hate me in his heart, according as were the signs which I did perceive in him."

Enan laid it upon his servant, that was ill-favored, to prepare the table and set it; whereupon he prepared it, and set upon it cloths so filthy and rotten, thou wouldst say they were found in the dunghill. So we sate us, each at his place, and he set before us unleavened bread, which giveth no pleasure. Then said he to the servant, who was duller than the sands of the sea, "Bring me of the pottage which I do love, and of the greens which I covet to eat, for in the land whence I am now come I have tasted naught, neither have I found aught of green herbage, neither have I seen there rain or lightning." Then the servant took a bowl, which was black as a crow from all sides and within; whereupon I did say, "The lettuce will harm me, nor will the vinegar aid me." But he said, "How may it harm? Is its name not merciful? * It guardeth men from evil humors, from black choler and red bile."

Quoth I, "May the Lord have no mercy upon him that planted it and removed it not from the number of herbs. For it doth dim the vision, and induce gout, and cause constipation, and darken the blessings of womb and breasts; it is called *lettuce*, for that it partaketh of the nature of swine, from which wise men keep far removed. Furthermore, this is not the paschal eve; wherefore the unleavened bread and bitter herbs?" When I had spoken thus he answered with angry and contentious speech: "I understand thee not; of all the evil foods thou knowest well, but of the good, which every understanding heart doth know, thou hast learned naught."

But I said, "Nay, in good truth I have learned the good also; but of the evil I am the more mindful, for that it behooveth me to beware of them and to keep far from their noxious harmfulness." Then said he, "Now do I perceive that thou lovest naught but to be sated with bread and flesh; and just Solomon hath said (Proverbs 13:25), 'The righteous eateth to the satisfaction of his soul; but the belly of the wicked shall want.' "

Said I, "Good and beloved sir, nor do I ask aught but to satisfy my soul." And to provoke him I did devour the entire bowl. Then said he to me loudly and in rebuke, "Therefore is its name called *lettuce*, for after thou hast rejected it, hast

* This and the following passages turn upon puns easily perceived in the original.

thou returned and devoured it." But I said, "Sir, because that thou hast said, 'It arouseth appetite,' have I eaten it; I do esteem it," quoth I, "with undying affection."

Then did he summon the slave, filthy with sweat, and said to him, "Remove this dish: thou hast brought it full and dost remove it empty; I did fear lest this man devour its very self. And now hasten to fetch another course, and delay not." To me he said, "Truly hath the Sage said, 'There is no trait as evil as haste, and none as good as delay.' "

But I said, "Of how many and goodly things is a man deprived because of sloth and tarrying! Therefore when a man doth behold aught that is goodly, let him hasten to seize it with an eager soul. For the Sage hath said, 'When thou hast plenty eat not till thou be hungry, but if thou art in want eat whenever thou canst.' Yea, and Solomon hath said (Proverbs 21:25), 'The desire of the slothful killeth him; for his hands refuse to labor.' "

Said he unto me, "Eat what thou findest this night, cloth, table, lamp and all, till thy great and fearful belly be filled. Another time I shall feed thee according to thy lust, with the help of the Rock, and I will satiate thee till they paunch be stuffed; for whom time hangs heavy a table should ever be ready set." Quoth I, "Praised be He who knoweth whether I shall dine tomorrow, or whether I may behold dawn with my eyeballs. True have our sages spoken: 'Neither say, "When I have leisure I will study"; perchance thou wilt nevermore have leisure.' "

Then said he to me, "Thou declarest thou art a great sage, and hast turned thy heart to the healing art, and in thy youth bestowed thy wealth on study; tell me therefore, surely thou knowest the saying of wise Diogenes, that whosoever restraineth his appetite and controlleth his belly, his virtues increase and he bringeth good health unto all his members. Furthermore saintly Hippocrates hath said, 'Let not an unnatural matter beguile thee, such as the ravenous hunger of the diseased ere he is cured.' " But I said to him, "Is it not himself that hath said, 'Strength is to the sick what provisions are to the wayfarer; the disease is the way, and therefore it behooveth the wise physician to guard his patient's strength, that it perish not ere the disease have come to its end'?" "But," quoth he, "Knowest thou not the saying of Hippocrates, 'In bodies which are not free of humors, the disease is increased in the same degree as the food is increased'?"

I said, "Thou hast spoken true, but our sages have said, may their memory be for a blessing, 'Yield the sick part of his desire, for a food which is desired, even if it be noxious, is better than one which is loathed, even if it be salutary.' " Said he to me, "Thou speakest true, yet bodies whose nature is of abundant humor, are so maintained by food, which then profiteth them naught." "But," said I, "the sages have said, 'Leave the drugs in the chemist's pot, if so thou can heal thy patient with food.' Yea, and Galen hath said, 'Leave thine entrails no long time without food, for when thou givest food to the members thou dost thereby withdraw from them all evil humors, and when the food enters in it destroyeth them.' Furthermore, much fasting enfeebles the body."

Enan said, "I see that thy belly is wicked, and lusteth ever to eat, and thine entrails are ever ready for food; I fear for thee, lest grave and hurtful diseases befall thee; and men say, 'Just as it behooveth not the judge to be a whoremonger, so behooveth it not the physician to follow after his appetites.' " But I answered him, "I eat in the name of Him who did feed manna to our fathers, and I yield to the words of no physician, for I know that when my time to die shall come, I may not escape, though I ruled the world."

Enan spake, "Surely thou hast heard the saying of Hippocrates: 'If thou lovest to eat, eat not until thou canst eat no more.' And Plato hath said, 'I eat that I may live; I do not live that I may eat.' Therefore haste not so eagerly to eat, but follow rather the wise tailor, who doth consider his measures full oft ere he cutteth his cloth, for there is no good in haste, and everyone that hasteth is delayed and doth rue it." Then said I to him: "Aristotle hath said that man is a living creature endowed with senses and knowledge, sound reason, and the capacity for growth through food and motion. And since man knoweth his body may not abide forever, he desireth that his form should abide, to fulfill which desire he requireth seed, which may not be attained except by growth, which may not be achieved except by food; the occasion for food then, is the desire to abide permanently in this world."

"Freely do I admit thy truth," said he, "nor may I deny that man may neither live nor exist but by food; they say that a healthy man may live but seven days without food, five without drink, and three without sleep. Nevertheless, it behooveth a wise man to control his desires with propriety and fitness, that he be temperate, moderate, and restrained in food and in drink; otherwise these will surely bring him to an early grave." "All this," said I, "is vanity and reason distorted. It was uttered as a curse (Leviticus 26:26), 'They shall deliver you your bread again by weight: and ye shall eat and not be satisfied.' "

Then said he to me, "Of whom didst thou learn this folly thou utterest? Thou hast surely not been initiated into the secret of wisdom. Knowest thou not that curse spoke of neediness and lack, and not of restraining and confining the appetite?" "Be silent," said I, "and restrain thy speech, for it is all vanity of vanities; as the proverb hath it, 'Women mind their distaffs, even in their speech': a generous man would have none of this." Quoth he, "Full well I know thou knowest women's proverbs better than men's."

"Good sir," said I, "I marvel greatly at thy slave, that he tarryeth so long, and I fear lest some mishap hath befallen him, even though he be sturdy as an oak." But his anger was kindled against me, and he answered me full wroth: "Why showest not fear of speaking of my servant? Indeed he is my helpmeet and my choice delight. Surely, wise men rather desire to hear words of wisdom and discretion than lust after eating and drinking. The philosopher hath said that wisdom refresheth the soul even as food refresheth the body." But he called to the slave and bade him: "Haste as I commanded thee, do as I instructed thee; bring the mutton speedily." "My lord," said the slave, "I shall do so."

Then said Enan to me, "Hast heard these sayings? Galen was asked, 'What is the greatest cure?' 'Moderation in food and drink,' he answered. And a certain sage hath said, 'Who minisheth his eating will lengthen his time of eating and will abide in health: who endureth the bitterness of medicaments will afterwards enjoy peace.' And when a sage who was sick was asked, 'Dost desire any foods?' he replied, 'I do indeed desire, but I take care lest I eat.' And our sages of blessed memory have said, 'Minish thine eating and thou wilt minish thy disease.' And also, 'Minish thine eating and thy counsel will be improved.' Furthermore, wisdom and counsel abide not in a full belly. A certain wise man who was a philosopher once said four things, which are: 'Impose not on thy stomach what it may not carry; do naught that hath not some advantage; have no faith in a woman, even if she be wise; and be not beguiled by wealth, even if it be great.' And when a very old man was asked, 'Whereby hast thou attained to length of days?' he answered, 'I have never eaten except I was hungry, and ever I left the table though appetite still remained.' Yohani likewise hath said, 'The best of remedies for digestion is that a man eat not until he be hungry, and leave his food before he be sated.'

"Furthermore a certain king once assembled four wise and understanding physicians, the first of Rome, the second of Ind, the third of Araby, and the fourth of Babylonia. He said to them, 'Let each of you mention a remedy which is without evil effect.' The Roman said, 'Hot water is a remedy which giveth no pain.' The Indian said, 'A remedy which is accompanied by no disease is kernel of prosper.' Quoth the Arab, 'Black halil * is a remedy free from pain.' But the Babylonian was the wisest of all, and kept silent. The king asked, 'Where-

* Arab herbs; authorities differ in their identification.

fore dost not thou declare thine opinion also?' Said he, 'Hot water corrodeth the entrails, and seeds of prosper cause moistness, and black halil rendereth the stomach soft.' 'What then is thy remedy?' asked the king. He replied, 'A remedy which is salutary for the entire body and which is accompanied by no pain or disease is: When thou sittest at thy table and desirest thy food, thou shouldst arise from it and leave it. Further, he that putteth all his desire in the filling of his belly, that which cometh from his belly is better than he.' And one of the Indian sages hath said, 'Afflicting oneself with hunger sets the seal to good health.' Yea, and Plato hath said, 'It behooveth a lover of mankind to consider his food as it were a remedy, in regard to which it is not his pleasure that it be abundant or sweet, but rather it holdeth his faith and his hope; so in food, let him not look for abundance or sweetness, but rather for effectiveness.' Regarding this hath the poet sung:

Have no fear to eat the bitter,
For full oft it proveth better,
For ailing folk than what is sweeter.

Sages say, "Prefer the bitter";
To make man better 'tis much fitter,
In wit feater, in figure neater.

"And when Galen was asked, 'Wherefore dost thou so stint thy food?' he replied, 'My purpose in eating is that I live: the purpose of others is to live in order to eat.' Plato hath said, 'It is not seemly, for the health of our bodies, that we abstain from food and drink, but for the wellbeing of our souls, let us not indulge therein overmuch.' And wise Diogenes hath said, 'A man's virtue is as the predominance of his reason over his desire; his weakness as the rule of his desire over his reason.' In the books of the wise men of India there was found written: 'He that attendeth not to hearken to the words of his friends in the hour of counsel, and to physicians in the hour of illness, and to the doctors of law in the hour of doubt, he will err in his counsel, his disease will increase, his error will be augmented.'

"Further, Hajjaj ibn Yussuf said to his physician Tajadun, 'I am overpowered by a desire to eat vermillion clay, but I would injure my soul; hast thou a remedy?' Said the physician, 'Lord king, thou dost overwhelm the mighty and destroy the heroes, terrify them that rise against thee and inspire dread in them that envy thee; over all art thou lord and ruler — yet desire of mud doth overwhelm thee!' 'Yet what may the remedy be?' asked the king. 'Dost assure me thou wilt not be wroth?' asked the physician. 'Aye, else I had never asked thee,' said the king. 'Then,' said the physician, 'no wise man nor mighty man doth eat of it, but only fools.' Then was the king abashed and ashamed, and swore he would nevermore eat of it. Socrates too hath said, 'He that enjoyeth all that he desireth, will suffer all manner of pain, but he that restraineth his desire augmenteth his glory and his fame.' Also, with desire goeth mishap, with counsel peace. Hippocrates hath said, 'Normal wealth is that a man labor that he hunger not nor be afflicted; further labor profiteth naught.' Therefore doth it behoove a wise man to labor only for what he requireth for his body's sake, and let him save his belly, for that is good for his honor and comely for his glory.

"Furthermore the philosopher Bedunis hath said, 'Reason perisheth by lust and desire, for reason maketh thee to rule over the season, and desire causeth thee to serve the season.' And Plato hath said, 'The body is the contrary of the soul; the one is not improved but by the destruction of the other. Therefore attend ye to the destruction of your bodies in the interest of your souls. Bring the dead out of his grave for the needs of the living, but put not the living to death for the sake of the dead.' Socrates hath said, 'He that hasteth for his desires' sake will haste yet more to rue him of his deeds.' Diogenes was asked, 'What is wealth?' 'To refrain from desire,' he replied. He that filleth his belly each day undermineth his body's structure and destroyeth it. And Aristotle hath said, 'When a thing befall, and thou knowest not of whom to take counsel, keep him removed that is nigh unto thy desires, and thy counsel will be goodly; for lust and desire are foes to reason.' Plato was asked 'Wherefore is everyman's counsel better for others than for himself?' 'Because another's counsel is without the bias of his own desires,' he replied. The choicest among men is he that ruleth over his desires and serveth not his own pleasure. If choice were given to a lustful man, he would choose not to lust. Plato hath said, 'May I not survive the day that I despise what I have praised or praise what I have despised; for then, upon that day, desire would have prevailed over reason.' Therefore praise not a thing, except thou hast known it; then it were true love.

"Hippocrates hath said, 'Let no man trust in his wisdom until his reason have prevailed over his desire.' As a stone will not retain water until it be rendered like unto a sponge, so will wisdom not retain itself to those who pride themselves thereon. Just as wisdom prospereth not with one that is silent, so do reason and wisdom not prosper for a soul that is sated. And just as the lamp furnisheth no light in the midst of the water, so doth wisdom shed no light among the proud and haughty of spirit. So hath Solomon said (Proverbs 11:2): 'When pride cometh, then cometh shame; but with the lowly is wisdom.' "

"Good sir," said I, "I see that thy slave lad is wanton and rebellious, or perhaps some mischance hath befallen him. Bid him let the food be till the morrow, for lo, the morning star hath risen." So he called his slave again, and did rebuke him, and arose from his place to smite him, and he besought my mercy, but I believed him not, for seven abominations were in his heart.

Then did the slave hasten and bring a sheep, roasted entire, head, knees, entrails, and all. Quoth Enan, "As my soul liveth and the soul of my grandfather, all my admonitions to beware of thy desire I gave thee only for thine own benefit and thine own good." But I replied to him, "Thy love is as the love of the demon for his son: he doth embrace him and caress him until that he doth strangle him."

Said Enan, "Knowest the five things of which Aristotle said, 'They are wasted and avail naught?' " "Nay," said I, "I know not. Prithee tell me what they may be." Quoth he, "Rain upon an ass, a lamp by the light of the sun, a virgin wedded to one that is impotent, savory pottage placed before one that is drunk, and a kindness done to one who doth not perceive it." He continued, "All that I have said thou hast weighed in the balance of blame, and hast recognized neither kindness nor goodness. Nevertheless, inasmuch as thou art become my guest, and art come unto my house, it is my duty to watch over thee and to guard thy body and thy soul; but if thou accept not my admonition, then is thy blood upon thine own head. Therefore, beware of the eating of flesh; as Hippocrates hath said, 'Guard ye from eating flesh and make not your bellies burial places for cattle.' And Galen hath said, 'There is no fool as the man who filleth his belly with whatever he find, and doth rely that the red bile will digest the things that are sour, and the white bile the things that are salt, and the black bile the things that are greasy and fat.' For red bile is as the eagle: a stork may appease it, yet a heron may provoke it; and the black bile is as an ox: a mere lad may lead it, but when it is in rut, even a strong man may not stand before it; and white bile is like the lion: if it be not slain it slays. Therefore master the white bile as thou dost master thy slave, and make thy peace with the black bile as thou makest peace with an enemy, and humble thyself to the red bile as thou dost humble thyself to one that is greater than thee. The combination of many diverse victuals, inasmuch as they are not of a simple sort, doth restrain the stomach from digesting them, and render it unable to transmute them into blood. Eat no hard substances, for they do destroy the teeth and corrupt the digestion. Divide thine eating into thirds: a third for food, a third for drink, a third for rest. It availeth not if the belly become swollen or if thou visit the latrine oft."

So he purposed to refrain me from food by his words, as he had done continually, and to deceive me with his discourse.

Wherefore I put my hands forth to the shoulders of the mutton, that I might eat of them; but he said to me, "Beware lest thou eat of them, for they do contain the humors of the heart." So I reached for the breast, but he said, "Touch it not, even in thy dreams, for it delayeth digestion in the stomach." I raised my hands to the kidneys, whereupon he said, "They are the source of the urine, and the refuse of the blood." I lifted my hands to the knees; but said he, "They are very near the bowels, whence issueth the dung." So I turned my hand back to take of the tail, which continueth the spine. "Of no good is the spine," said he, "for it is filthy and bad and doth kill the wicked desire of him that taketh it. Therefore do the Chaldaeans call it *lekinah* for that it causeth weeping and lamentation."

Then said I, "Inasmuch as thou wouldst not that I eat of it, wherefore hast thou served it, or wherefore roasted it?" "Eat," said he, "of the portions that profit, as the hind legs and forelegs, which have naught of evil." So I stretched my hand forth to take of the legs which were nearest me, but he said, "Take not of the forelegs, but of the hind legs, for they are better; and take not the right, for the left is better, for that it is nearer the heart and the source of natural warmth; or better, take what portion I give thee, and leave the rest, and thereby be delivered from its evil." So he reached forth for the left leg, which was dry and scorched, and gave it me, and I ate it as a dog eateth a bone. Then he hastened and said to his servant, "Speedily remove the mutton, lest aught of its evil nature escape." But when I saw this shameful deed, I said in my heart, "It is but left me that I make my face brazen toward this niggard, whose soul doth mourn over a little flesh"; so I cried with a loud voice and a bitter soul, "Am I a dog that thou givest me bones? Is it written in any of the books of wisdom that men are to be fed on the bones of beasts and cattle? Give me flesh, for my soul doth long for it, else I take it by violence." And I reached forth and seized of the flesh ere it was removed from before me. Enan spoke up,

"Against whom criest thou, and speakest words of boldness?" And I said, "It is not mine to abide this."

Then said he to his household, "Have ye seen this lunatic that hath come unto my table to plunder and to rob my substance? All that was before me he did snatch and devour. Truly sayeth the proverb, 'We have purchased a cock, but he remaineth as partner in our domicile.' "

Then did he glower upon me with his eyes, and gnash his teeth, and swore an oath saying, "Hadst thou not come under the shelter of my roof beam and wert thou not in my house, I would chastise thee with rods and reprove thee as one of the fools." He continued in his speech to me, "Truly hath the Parsee sage said, 'The departure of a fool is better than the company of a wise man.' "

Then did I fear in my heart from before the sound of his words, and my soul nigh went from me when I heard his speech; I strengthened my heart, though no spirit was in me, and said, "Thou dost indeed not know who I may be, in that thou dost threaten to chastise me with rods; surely, I am Joseph, the Mighty, who did smite the lion within the pit."

But he replied, "Woe to the season when sheep and kidlets slay mighty lions." Then he continued, "Lo, I see thou takest pleasure in roast flesh, and dost disregard all diseases and maladies; do thou then eat thy fill of it, nor give thy stomach aught of rest; perhaps then there will befall thee what befell the king, whose joy was turned to sorrow and sighing." I asked, "And what did befall him?" He spake:

"Once a gardner came unto his garden in the winter season and there found lilies, and his heart rejoiced exceedingly when he saw them. So he gathered them, and disposed them in a handsome bowl, and brought them to the king, and placed them before him. The king marveled at them, and they were pleasing in his eyes, and he commanded that a hundred pieces of silver be given the gardner.

"Then said the king in his heart, 'This is a joyous and gladsome day': so he made a great feast, and sat him to eat and to drink with his faithful ministers, and to rejoice in the festival of lilies. And the king had an only daughter, who happened to be big with child; so he said unto his servants, 'Call the young woman, that she may rejoice with us.' So his daughter came and sat before him; and he set before her the bowl of lilies, and to her it was more precious than pearls. Then she put forth her hand to take one of the lilies to smell of it, and there sprang up upon her face a serpent which was amongst the lilies. Her heart went out and she trembled, and she cried in her pains, for her travail was come upon her. But the child came forth from her womb and died, and the joy was turned to sorrow and sighing."

When Enan perceived that I regarded not all that he had spoken, and that I remained stiff-necked despite all his words, he said unto me, "Eat thou all the sheep; take no pity upon it nor spare it, for ofttimes a single eating restraineth many eatings." So he said to his slave, "Bring all that thou hast." The slave then brought a great bowl, like as a hogshead, filled with the flesh of an ox. As soon as it reached me, I reached forth my hand and my knife and began to eat of it.

But Enan said to me, "Beware of eating beef, for it is the source of every pain and doth beget maladies of the hands and of the feet and of the joints which do bind the members together, and it causeth diseases of the mouth and paralysis and constipation. Therefore fill not thy belly more, which indeed is open like a gate to devour all, but rather hearken to my counsel, and let not thine evil inclination beguile thee; put not into thy mouth that which will corrupt thy flesh." So he called to his servant and said, "Remove far from him this despised and rejected food and cause this death to depart from us."

Then did I take a joint of the meat into my hand and eat it to satisfy my soul. When he perceived that I was eating to satiety, his wrath was kindled so that he was well nigh seized of an evil spirit, and he cried out and said, "Who hath made thee to have dominion in my house? Meseemeth 'tis of thee that the poet hath sung:

> Lo this dull and witless wight
> Beguiled me by his tongue's smooth might
> Craving of food but a single bite.
>
> Like Eden's garden my board in haste
> I arrayed, but like Sahara's waste
> His gluttony left it, bare and chaste.

And again:

> The fellow hath charged upon my board
> In panoply full, like a warrior lord.
> He did eat
> My bread and meat;
> Victuals he devoured all my hoard.

Then he continued, "O thou who art wanting in heart, what will it profit thee if thou be surfeited and grow fat? Mayhap disease will leave its mark in thy bowels, and thou wilt rue thy gluttonous eating when thy malady is great, and thou wilt return to thy leanness and thy poverty and wilt bewail thy lust and thy appetite when thy flesh and body fail thee. Aye, what befell the fox will surely befall thee also." "And what befell the fox?" I inquired. He said:

"A certain fox was lean and poor of flesh. Ever did his food fail, and by reason of dire want was he reduced to the proportions of a hare. On a day his heart moved him to depart from his surroundings, so he turned hither and thither, and saw a certain garden, at whose goodliness and comeliness he marveled. He rejoiced in its fruits and delicious foods, but its walls were high, so that he availed not to overleap them and enter into the garden. So he went about the garden walls until that he found a certain breach, whereby he entered; and when he was come into the garden he did eat and become satisfied and grow fat: all the day he did but eat and sleep. But when harvest time came, there came the master of the garden to gather in his grapes from the vineyard which was in the garden. When the fox beheld the harvesters he was seized with great pain and agony, 'For,' said he, 'now will they discover me and will surely slay me for to take my skin.' So he returned to the breach in the wall to depart as he had entered, but could not because of his excess of flesh and his fat; wherefore his agony and sorrow waxed greater. He fasted for three days and three nights, and afflicted his soul until that he returned to his pristine poverty and leanness; then did he depart by that same breach by which he had entered, weeping and wailing: 'Woe betide me! What availed it me that I did eat and drink and grow fat and gross? Lo, I have returned to poverty, even as I was aforetime.'

"Therefore," said Enan, "hearken unto my counsel and rebuke thy lust that it persuade thee not, and guard thee from diseases occasioned by change of habits."

But I said to him, "Utter no word of ill omen! Nay, I fear rather for my desire, lest it wane and diminish."

Chapter IX

Enan proveth Zabara's knowledge of medicine and nature by two and thirty questions.

Then said Enan to me, "Thou hast declared that thou art wise, expert in the healing art: Do thou then answer to what I shall ask of thee, that I may gauge thine understanding and discernment." Said I, "Food doth withhold me from answering; for my bowels are become warm from having been afflicted. Leave me until that I have satisfied my longing; then will I answer thine every query."

But he said, "After that thou art full and surfeited, thou wilt naught declare nor wilt thou avail to show thine opinion." "The hungry man doth pant after food," said I, "and understandeth no saying, even if he be such a one as Heman or Chalcol." "But," quoth he, "how long wilt thou eat? Woe to thy belly, for it will never have rest."

But when I had eaten and was satisfied, and had nigh perished of abundance of food, I spake to him, "Good sir, sleep seizeth upon mine eyelids. By thy leave I will go up to my couch, and I will lay me down, and my sleep will be sweet unto me." But he said, "How wilt thou not be sleepy, seeing thou hast left no morsel uneaten? Nay, as my soul liveth, thou shalt not ascend thy couch until that I have questioned thee, and proved thy wisdom, and have perceived whether all these victuals have entered the paunch of a wise man or of a fool."

Then said I to him, "Be thy questions deep as the pit or lofty and exalted, I will make answer to each. Yet make not thy discourse overlong; for Night hath spread her wings and Dawn rubbeth her eyelids."

1. He asked, "Knowest thou wherefore the two veins of the eyes differ from all other veins of the body, in that they are open?" I replied: "Because of the power of vision which

is transmitted from the brain to the eyes by means of them."

2. "Dost know of the disorder of the eyes which is called *Ahwal* in Arabic? Wherefore are two images of single objects seen by those who suffer from this disorder?" Said I, "Because that the veins are not equal, and do not go to the eyes by a parallel route, but one goeth down while the other goeth up; therefore doth the one eye behold an object from above while the second eye beholdeth it from beneath. The proof is, if one eye be covered the patient will perceive but one object only."

3. Said he, "Dost know the cause of sneezing?" I replied, "A humor or current of air which is of a nature harmful to the brain is therefore pressed thence to the bone which is perforated like a colander; from which perforations the humors of the head issue forth through the nostrils; and because the perforations in that bone are small in compass nature requireth to expel them with great violence, wherefore is the sound of sneezing audible."

4. "Wherefore are there three molar teeth in the upper jaw and but two in the lower?" Said I, "Because that the upper teeth are dependent and therefore require reinforcement whereas the lower teeth are firmly set, and therefore require no reinforcement."

5. "Knowest wherefore it is, that when a man openeth his mouth, the breath that cometh forth is warm, whereas if he shut his lips and expel his breath, it is cool?" Said I, "The breath that cometh forth from the mouth of man is ever warm, for it is warmed by the heat of the heart; but when he compresseth his lips to breathe it forth, he doth expel it and thus stir the atmosphere and set it in motion, and whatsoever stirreth the atmosphere and setteth it in motion doth cool it. Therefore doth it come about that it is cool."

6. "The same wind which is warm elsewhere is cool in the bathhouse: wherefore?" "Because the atmosphere of the bathhouse is even warmer than the wind, wherefore it doth seem cool by comparison."

7. "Wherefore is it, that when a man doth meditate on a matter which he knoweth not he doth incline his head forward, whereas if he think of a matter which he hath known and forgot he raiseth his head?" I replied, "When a man meditateth upon a thing which he knoweth not, he requireth to bring his reasoning power, which resideth in the middle sac of the brain, in conjunction with the imaginative power, which resideth in the first sac, in the place of the forehead. But when a man doth meditate on a matter which he hath known but forgot, he requireth to bring his reasoning power in conjunction with his recalling power, which resideth in the hindmost sac, situated near the back of the neck; and when the reasoning and recalling powers are conjoined, he doth recall the matter. This secret is unknown to many physicians who are wise in their own eyes and understanding in their own sight."

8. "How many are the canals of the bowels?" he asked. "Three, I replied; one lengthwise to receive the food, and one diagonal to retain it until it be digested, and the third crosswise to force the food on and expel it when it hath been digested."

9. "What is the number of the intestines?" "Six: three above being fine and three below gross."

10. "Wherefore is only one convoluted?" Said I: "The convoluted one is near the liver and from it the liver doth draw the essence of the aliment; if it were straight, as are the others, the aliment would go through so hastily that the liver would have no time to withdraw the essence of the aliment."

11. "How may the essence of the aliment reach to the liver, seeing the intestines have no perforation whence it may issue, nor hath the liver a perforation through which it may enter?" Said I, "By that hidden force which the Arabs call energy. No man may know it, for it hath no natural explanation; just as the lodestone which draweth iron with no natural force whatever but with the force called energy. Similarly the stone called diamond may not be broken by iron, but it is broken and shattered by lead."

12. "Wherefore is the urine restrained from being voided when the bladder is completely filled, so that the person cometh into danger?" Said I, "Because the mouth of the bladder is a complex of fibers; and when the volume is filled, the fibers draw together from all sides, so that the mouth of the bladder is stopped and the urine may not be voided."

13. "When a man doth dream that he lieth with a woman, he dischargeth his semen involuntarily; but when he doth dream that he covereth his feet, nothing doth come forth. Yet urine is more abundant than semen, and sharper, and its going out is nigher?" Said I, "This matter is very deep and only a chosen few among all physicians understand it, for it is a great secret; yet will I reveal it to thee, so that thou mayst know thy food hath been eaten of a wise man and not of a fool. Know then that the nature of a man doth govern his body, both when he is awake and when he is asleep; when he is asleep nature doth keep guard over the entire body, that nothing issue forth from his private parts without his will. But if a man dream that he lie with a woman, despite all, his semen issueth forth; for all the members desire it to issue forth for their own pleasure, as doth his nature also, for desire doth draw it together from all the members, and gather it, and bring it to the private parts, where it is transformed, just as blood is transformed in the breast of a woman until it become milk; and of the members none doth restrain the semen. But in the case of urine, it is only the one member which desireth it to issue forth and but the portion of nature which that member containeth; all the other members and their portions of nature do refrain it and restrain its issuing forth; therefore may it not issue forth until the man awake. Not so infants, whose nature and members are both weak. And this is the true cause, which is hidden from the wise men."

Then said he, "I will ask you yet other things, graver and more difficult." "Ask as thou choosest," said I, "for I will answer and not delay."

14. "Said he, "Dost know wherefore the spleen is called

the laughing organ?" I replied, "The sages have given two reasons. First, it is the source of the black bile, which doth beget folly; laughter is folly, wherefore thou perceivest that the fool doth ever laugh; and so hath Solomon said, (Ecclesiastes 2:2) 'I said of laughter, It is mad.' The second reason is that the spleen doth assemble all the black bile which is in the body, such as sorrow and sighing, so that the remainder of the body becometh free of it and thereupon man desireth to laugh and rejoice."

15. "Wherefore doth a little lad eat more than a grown man?" "Because the lad requireth his food for two purposes, to carry on life and for growth, whereas the man requireth his food only to carry on life."

16. "Wherefore is it, when a man ascendeth to a high place he becometh faint and weary and his ascent is difficult; whereas when he goeth down, he becometh not weary and his descent is easy?" I replied, "Because it is the nature of man to walk upright, and when he goeth up he must needs incline forward and his height is reduced, which is not in accordance with his wont and nature; therefore doth he grow faint and weary. But when he goeth down he standeth upright, and he groweth not wearied, for that he walketh as is his wont."

17. "How may a physician know whether a plague cometh as the result of corruption and alteration of the atmosphere or from corruption and alteration of food stuffs?" I replied: "If the plague cometh from corruption and change in the atmosphere, then will all the sick die of a single malady, for the atmosphere is the same for all. But if the cause be corruption and change in food stuffs, they will die of diverse diseases; for they have not all eaten of a single victual, and according as is the diversity of victuals and their changes will be the diversity of their diseases."

18. "Wherefore is the neck between the head and the breast?" Said I "If the head were very near the breast, and there were naught to intervene between them, then were the mist from the heart and its smoke very hot. But the length

of the neck doth separate them, and the heat is diluted by the intervening space and is cooled. Similarly is the thick vapor of the blood clarified and weakened by the space. An analogy is the smoke which issueth from fire: When it is near the fire it is very thick, but as it goeth farther upward it becometh clearer, and simpler, and weaker. The neck also hath a function in issuing forth the voice, for without it the voice were inaudible."

19. "Wherefore are teeth not formed when the embryo is created?" "Because they would injure the mother in nursing, and there is no need of them then to cut food and grind it."

20. "Whereof are the teeth formed?" "Teeth are formed from the remains of thick and hard foods, and the heat of the nursing milk causeth them to sprout and grow forth. Therefore many children grow them much more quickly than others, who tarry. Those who nurse of hot milk grow their teeth more speedily, and they who nurse of cold milk tarry in their growing of teeth."

21. "Wherefore are the wide cutting teeth formed before the dog teeth and the molars?" I replied, "The thing thou speakest of happens for two reasons. First, the infant at the beginning is of a soft and moist nature and its nourishment is moist food, and it is unable to produce anything strong and thick and hard from its excess nourishment until that it is nourished with dry food. Of such food the excess is thick and hard, and is the substance whence the molar teeth are formed; but the thin and sharp teeth are formed of a thin and weak substance. Secondly, man at first doth cut his food and grind it afterwards; but the young infant is not able to grind but only to cut, and therefore is he sustained by food moist and well cooked or chewed in his mother's mouth. Therefore hath he no need of grinding teeth, for nature maketh naught in vain. Another reason is as follows: at first the heat of the infant is scant and feeble, and heat that is feeble may only cause feeble things to grow; thereafter when his heat has increased the child produceth what is larger and firmer."

22. "Why do the teeth of children fall out after a certain period, after which others grow in their places?" I replied: "The original teeth are formed from a tenuous substance; being feeble, as we have mentioned above, they cannot then be strong, and therefore do they fall out. Regarding the growth of the second teeth this is the cause. When a child's food becomes thicker and harder, firmer teeth grow and increase, for his nature is then firmer. Furthermore the strong and hard substance doth expel the slight and feeble substance and cast it forth; and therefore do the weak teeth fall out, because the strong and hard substance doth oppress them, as happeneth also to the hairs in early infancy. In old age the teeth fall out by reason of dryness, just as the hair also falleth out by reason of the dryness which doth prevail over the elderly. This befalleth plants also, as for instance *boraje*, in time of drouth."

23. "Wherefore," he asked, "are tears of sorrow salt?" "Because the liver and heart which have grown hot by reason of the sorrow do heat the tears excessively until that they become salt. But tears which spring from a heart joyous and glad are sweet. So hath the philosopher written."

24. "Wherefore is salt water heavier than fresh water?" I said, "Because it is thick and impure, whereas fresh water is thin and pure. The proof is as follows: Take salt and powder it, and mingle it with fresh water until it is well mixed, and then cast eggs into that water; the eggs will float on salt water, for it is thick and impure; they settle on the water as it were clay, and cannot sink for the thickness of the water. In fresh water eggs sink. Another greater proof: The Philistine Sea is very bitter and salt; if a man or beast be bound hand and foot and cast into this sea he will float, being light in comparison to the salt water. No fish are found therein for that it is exceeding salt."

25. "Is salt water cold or hot?" Said I, "Very hot; not because of the vapor which doth envelop it, but the force of the earth whence it issueth doth cause it to form a skim. Furthermore, rivers and fountains possess different qualities in

taste and appearance; the cause for this is the variety of natural heat in the respective places, which doth affect them. For the earth is like a thing which is burned by the heat of fire; its qualities change as doth the burning; it groweth hard and, as it were, congealeth, as into ashes or alum or the like."

26. "Why is the snowlike foam formed?" "Because particles of pure water are sundered and air entereth into the interstices, wherefore it groweth white."

27. "Wherefore doth hail occur in the hot seasons, usually in the summer solstice, and but rarely in the cold season, when the genesis of hail is by reason of cold, when the water above the clouds doth congeal, which would be like to happen in cold seasons: wherefore are the seasons then reversed?"

I replied: "In the hot season the coolth of the atmosphere entereth into a cloud, for heat, which is its contrary and enemy, doth prevail over it and pursue it, whereupon the coolth fleeth and entereth into a cloud; there it doth congeal all that is therein, and render it hail. But in the cold season coolth is spread abroad everywhere, and not in the cloud only, and there is no heat from which it should take refuge within the cloud. The proof is, when water that is hot is put in a cool place, it cooleth more rapidly, for the coolth which confronteth the heat showeth forth ever-waxing power. Hence, when the atmosphere is hot, the water congealeth into hail rapidly."

Then he tried me further and said, "Art knowing in the wisdom of the Talmud?" "A little of it have I learned," said I, "but to my sorrow, not as much as I should like." Then said he, "Wilt thou ask of me, or shall I ask and thou answer?" "Ask as thy heart desireth," said I, "and I shall answer as I find words."

28. "Wherefore do the sages say, 'Bastards are for the most part clever?' " "Thou hast made thy questioning so difficult all the night," said I, "that I have come nigh to wishing for the grave." "Meseemeth," said he, "thine accuracy is wanting in this wisdom, and the strides of thy science are straitened; thy fountains have ceased, and therefore art thou

vexed." "I have not lost mine understanding," said I to him, "nor am I vexed; yet hath lust of sleep dimmed knowledge and discernment out of my heart. Nevertheless will I answer thy questioning, and refute thy foolish imaginings.

"Know then that a bastard springeth only from an adulterer and an adulteress, and adultery springeth only from the love of each for the other, and love springeth only from lust, and lust only from the heat of the heart; from the heat of the heart are all the blood and all the members warmed, and according as their lust is great so is their heat. Then are the two seeds warmed, that of the man and that of the woman, whence springeth the foetus. Therefore is the bastard clever because cleverness ariseth from the heat of the heart and the keenness of the reasoning which is in the brain. Similarly the bastard is tall, for by heat do all things wax tall and great. This is the cause wherefore the bastard is tall and clever."

29. "I will ask you another," said he, "even harder than this. Wherefore have the sages said, 'If the woman cast her seed first she will bear a male child, but if the man cast his seed first, she will bear a female child?' "

I replied: "If the seed of the woman issue from her eggs, which are the horns of the womb, and fall into the womb first, the womb closeth not over it until the male seed have entered in; by which time it is cooled a little and its natural vigor is become somewhat enfeebled. When the male seed entereth in and becometh commingled therewith, it prevaileth over it and rendereth it like unto its own nature by reason of its greater vigor and heat; and after the womb hath closed over both, a male child is conceived, for the seed of the man hath prevailed over the seed of the woman. Exactly the same reason applieth, that a female child be born when the man cast his seed first.

"Afterwards the power of change doth take hold of the seed, and formeth a skin about them exceeding fine, and congealeth them somewhat, that they be not spilled hither and thither. Thereafter doth the divine power of the Creator enter in, and form His likeness. But if the seed cleave not well to the womb, which is then closed after it, the woman will never at all conceive of that seed. Therefore have our sages — their memory be for a blessing — said, 'Seed which is not cast as an arrow is shot is no seed'; which signifieth, the woman will never at all conceive of it. Therein is the womb like as the stomach, for unless the food enter the very extremities of the stomach and be there retained, it will never at all be digested. Therefore, then, doth a man beget daughters, when, by the feebleness of his nature and his members, he availeth not to make the seed abide, but doth cast it forthwith. And thus the sages interpreted the verse (Psalms 127:3): 'Lo, male children are an heritage of the Lord, and the fruit of the womb is his reward': they are rewarded with male children for that they linger in the womb of the woman. Therefore also were the offspring of Lot's daughters males, for their father, being drunk, lingered much in the casting of seed, as is the wont of one that is drunk; and they, by reason of their great lust, did cast their seed first."

30. "Wherefore have the sages of blessed memory said regarding the citron, radish and egg, 'Were it not for their outer jacket they would never issue from the intestines?' What relation is there between an egg on the one hand, and a citron and radish on the other? For of the citron and radish the jacket is the best portion, and were it not that the blood were aroused by the heat occasioned by the jackets, the stomach could not digest them and they would issue from the intestines only after a very long time; whereas of the egg the shell is the worst portion?"

I replied, "The yellow of an egg is excellent aliment for the body and would be wholly rendered into blood, for that it is of the same nature. Were it not for its outer jacket (the white) which is hard to digest, and delayeth to issue from the stomach, the yellow would never at all come forth from the intestines, for it were wholly rendered into blood."

31. "Dost know," he asked, "wherefore the sages have said,

'Let blood the second day after eating fish?' For surely fish is very cool and doth cool the body; how then do they bid the eater to let blood, which is hot and the contrary of fish in all its effects?"

I answered: "Fish is a thick food and begetteth phlegmatic blood, wherewith the body and all its veins are filled; therefore did they command that blood be let on the second day, that that blood be diminished before it prevail over the whole body and work it harm. They advised letting the blood on the second day after eating the fish, because bloodletting doth weaken the entire body, and cleanse it, and warm it, and remove the blood from the veins, but the blood begot of the fish doth cool the body and fill the veins. This was said only of fish not overnoxious, such as the red fish and the like."

32. "Dost know the difference between the dumbness called apoplexy, and the slumber called sleep, and the disease called epilepsy?" I replied, "I know that sleep and epilepsy are contained in the sacs of the brain, and dumbness by the quivering of the intervening portions." *

* The last paragraph is quite unintelligible, owing to the faulty transmission of the many technical words employed, chiefly from the Arabic.

Chapter X

Zabara trieth Enan with questions of diverse sciences, of which Enan availeth not to answer even one.

I looked at Enan, and lo, slumber was lurking in his eye points and the lids were straining to caress the eyeballs; so I said in my heart, "I will prolong my discourse with the churl, and will not permit him to sleep: I will question him even as he hath questioned me, and prevent his slumbers even as he hath prevented mine." So I said to him, "Good master, will it please thee that I try thee as thou hast tried me and that I prove thee as thou hast proved me?" "Truly hast thou spoken," said he, "when thou didst declare that slumber withholdeth all knowledge and understanding. Yet ask me and try me; an thou wilt prove me, thou wilt discover me gold."

"In what science shall I question thee?" I asked. "In whatsoever thou wilt," he replied, "for I know the half of all wisdom." "Shall I ask thee of astronomy?" I asked. "As thou wilt," he replied, "ask."

1. "Wherefore may an eclipse of the sun occur only on the twenty-eighth day of the month, and an eclipse of the moon only the night of the fourteenth?" Said he, "I do not know."

2. "Wherefore doth the light of the moon wax night by night until mid-month, when it be all bright, and wane from mid-month onward until it be all darkened?" Said he, "I know not."

Said I, "Shall I ask thee of the science of geometry?" "Ask," said he.

3. "Knowest thou of that line which a man reckoneth in his heart but may not form with his hand, upon which line the entire science of geometry is based?" Said he, "I do not know."

4. "If a cylinder be two cubits in length and its diameter

a span, what is its circumference? What its shadow?" "I know not," said he.

"Shall I question thee in the science of sounds?" I asked. "Do," said he.

5. "Canst assort and classify the letters according to the organs of speech (as palatals, linguals, etc.)?" "No," said he.

6. "Dost know the sound which issueth from the gullet, but is represented by none of the letters?" "I do not," he said.

"I shall question thee in the science of logic; hast studied it?" "Aye," said he.

7. "Drippings which drop upon a stone do leave a mark thereon and dig a furrow therein: did the very first dripping leave a mark or not?" "I do not know."

"Of what science then shall I question thee?" "Of reckoning," said he, "for therein am I wise and understanding."

8. "Dost know the sum of a third, and two-sixths and three-ninths?" "No," said he.

"Shall I ask thee of the knowledge of lunar intercalation," said I, "wherein we be more skilled than all peoples, even if it be not accounted among the sciences?" "Ask," said he.

9. "Wherefore have the sages said — their memory be a blessing: 'If the new moon be observed before midnight, the first of the month is fixed for that day; if it be observed after midnight, for the following day; except if the first new moon of the year be observed on a Monday, fifteen hours and five hundred eighty-nine seconds after nightfall, or more if the preceding year had been a leap year, when the New Year is postponed': Wherefore? Further, if New Year fall upon a Saturday or Monday, the year will be regular; if on a Tuesday, neither wanting nor full; if on a Thursday, the normal year cannot be wanting, but the leap year cannot be regular:* Wherefore?"

* The calculations are not mere gibberish, though very involved and though the difficulties are augmented by faulty transmission of the text. See the note of Davidson (p. 118). Enan's reply is justified by the fact that numerals are cited by combinations of letters of the alphabet, which are then pronounced as words, and naturally give a strange sound. Calendar and other rules were also cited by acrostic mnemonics, which were pronounced as words.

"How should I know thy questions," said Enan, "seeing I do not even understand thy language? Nay, methinks thy words are of no human speech at all; thou hast merely imagined them in thy heart." "Fool," said I, "they are the mnemonic signs which our sages have set for the intercalation of months." Then I continued, "But how hast thou declared thou knowest the half of all sciences, seeing thou knowest not a single thing?" "Aristotle hath said," he replied, " 'He that saith, "I know not," hath spoken the half of wisdom.' "

"Woe betide thee!" said I; "and was it this thou didst mean when thou didst declare thyself knowing the half of knowledge?" "Aye," said he.

"I adjure thee," said I, "as thy soul liveth and the soul of thy neighbor, speak only truth to me. Yet because the sages have said, 'An oath may not take effect over another,' I know that thou wilt fulfill thy first oath only." "And what may the oath be I swore first?" he asked. "Thou hast sworn," said I, "that no true word would ever issue from thy lips, and methinks thou dost ever keep that oath."

"Truly have the sages said," quoth he, "that a sage is better than a prophet. As my soul liveth, I have been bound by that oath these fifty years, and, the Lord be praised, I have kept it. Yet now will I tell thee the truth. Know that of all the sciences, I have learned only the science of medicine; that is my portion and my lot and therein am I expert. Of philosophy I have learned but two things and no more." "And what may they be?" I asked. "The one," he answered, "is: 'Naught have I found of better service to the body than silence'; and the other, 'Whoso is profuse of words causeth sin.' " "Would thou didst but fulfill that which thou has learned," said I; "but thou art such an one as the sages spoke of: 'Some discuss well but practice ill.' "

Said I, "Wilt thou then, that I question thee in the science of medicine, which thou declarest to be thy labor, thine honor and pride?" "Ask on," said he.

10. Said I, "Is childbirth, being a combination of three

diseases which are not natural, yet itself a natural malady?" Said Evans, "I know not."*

11. "Is great thirst caused by parching of the stomach or of the liver?" Said he, "I know not."

12. "Dost know what veins they are which it behooveth to bleed and what others it behooveth to feed and fatten?" Said he, "I know not."

13. "Is it an indication that the patient is healed when the white and smooth portion of the urine which usually sinketh to the bottom of the vessel, floateth on the surface, or is it not? Is it a bad sign when the dark portion which is wont to sink floateth, or is it not?" Said he, "I know not."

14. "Dost know wherefore in old age teeth do fall from the mortar of the jaw?" "No," said he.

15. "Wherefore are some veins bled longitudinally and others diagonally?" "I know not," said he.

16. "What stone is it, which, if a man look upon it, appeareth white, and if he look upon it further it appeareth ruddy, and if he look upon it still further it appeareth green, and if he look upon it very long it doth appear dusky and black?" Said he, "I do not know."

17. "Knowest thou the drug, which if it be put underneath a moist tongue, a man will perceive four diverse tastes,—sweet, and bitter, and salt, and sour?" "I do not know," he said.

18. "How many are the members of the eye, and what are its diseases?" "I do not know," he said.

19. "Wherefore is a fetus of seven months viable, whereas one of eight months, nigh onto nine, which is the natural period, is not viable?" Said he, "I do not know."

20. "Wherefor doth the creative force, which is divine, at times form twins in a mother's womb, and at times triplets and quadruplets? Galen reports that in his time a certain woman in Rome bore twenty children in five years, four at each birth, of which two were male and two female: how doth it come about?" "I do not know."

21. "Of how many sorts is the beat of the veins which do beat in the forearm of a man?" Said he, "I do not know."

Then said I, "He that knoweth none of these things withereth his days away in vanity and consumeth his years in emptiness. Didst thou not declare thyself a wise man, skillful to heal each disease or malady, to assuage pangs, and to relieve agony? But I perceive thou hast learned naught of the wisdom but to speak guile and deceit, to multiply thy sayings and thy discourses with a false and lying tongue, to frame utterances in language of vanity and emptiness; to gaze upon men and inquire of their maladies, to display to them decoctions and drugs, and species of herbs and spices; to blind their eyes and take their substance by saying unto them: 'This decoction availeth for a pain of the head, this drug removeth dimness of the eyes, this herb relieveth heaviness of the ears, this spice improveth bad breath, this is a balm for aching teeth, this will strengthen weakness of the lips, this will prevent pains in the hands and feet, this will restrain the disease of the bowels, this will heal fever, this will cause hair to grow on a bald pate, this will make a faint spirit robust, this will relieve a heart distressed with labor.'

"So do Quack and Cureall who come to the patient with their lies and their boldness, with their cunning speech and shameless falsehood, and gaze into his countenance, and open his eyelids and remove his finger nails to cause him to fear and tremble, and to hasten the day of his doom. Then take they a beaker of his urine, and raise it in their hands until it reach their beards, and shake it violently to make the water turbid, and they say, 'This is of the gravest of diseases'; whereas they have no knowledge of it except that it is urine, for that its odor hath reached their nostrils. Then say they unto his kinsmen and friends and neighbors, 'This malady is unknown to many physicians'; and thereby do they affright and confuse them. Then do they sigh deeply as they stand about the patient, and say to him: 'Guard thee from dwelling in the holes in the earth among rocks; attend speedily! give! give! spare not thy silver and thy gold, that thou mayst deliver thy soul from destruction and thy body from the valley of the shadow of death; for wherein will thy substance profit thee when the day of thy doom cometh, when the angel of death putteth his hand over thine eyes, and clotheth thy body, of which the frame is his, with clods of earth and with vermin? Give us of thy silver and thy gold, then will we remove disease from within thee.'

"So do they speak harsh words to their patients, and thereby ensnare souls; they heal without faith and without mercy for handfuls of barley and for pieces of bread. They slay the needy for a shekel or two of silver and the poor for a pair of shoes. May He that doth debase unto Sheol and doth exalt, visit their waywardness and deceitfulness upon them; may He plague them with the botch of Egypt and with the emerods, until that their bowels do issue from their privy parts. For that science which is exalted above all sciences, for which pearls nor coral can be an exchange, whose price is above rubies, have they made as it were but of the value of a sycamore. For him that is of their ilk hath Hippocrates said, 'A foolish physician is worse than the disease, for day by day doth he multiply destruction.' And of him too hath the poet said:

Be a successful doctor!
  So spake Chance to the Fool:
Grab what the patient has locked a-
  Way; away with medical school!

You may kill a man for to plunder him,
  Society will leave you at large;
You've a better thing than the Reaper grim:
  He can't charge.

Chapter XI

Zabara doth marvel that he hath heard no sound from his ass during the night, and upon investigation doth discover that Enan's servant hath so muzzled its mouth that it was like to perish of hunger. Zabara chideth Enan for his inhumanity and in the contention Enan doth declare that he is in good truth no human, but rather of the demons, of the seed of Asmodeus. Great dread falleth upon Zabara when he heareth this matter, but he is assured of Enan that no harm will befall him.

Said Enan to me, "How long wilt thou make thy face hard, and reproach me, and smite me with the rod of thy tongue? Yet will I bear thine abuse, for the sake of thy wisdom and thine understanding." Then did he bow his head and declare shamefacedly: "Thus and thus doth a man endure of his faithful friends. Nevertheless, much as I marvel at thy wisdom, yet am I the more amazed at thy voracity, for thou hast left nothing remaining, but hast cleared my table of all that was good, paying no heed to the proverb of Solomon (Proverbs 23:2): 'And put a knife to thy throat, if thou be a man given to appetite.' Thou deniest the words of the sage who hath said, 'Discernment and knowledge may not abide in a belly that is full and a soul that is sated.' " And I said, "How long wilt thou thus prate? And whereof is my belly full? Surely, in my hunger this night I have not eaten as much as would fill a single chamber of the chambers of my stomach."

Quoth he, "The good Lord deliver me from all trouble and affliction! Naught there is to which I may liken your belly save only the horseleech, and I do marvel at Solomon in that he saith (Proverbs 30:15): 'There are three things that are never satisfied, yea, four things say not.' It is enough. Wherefore did he not say five? Thy belly, which is never at all satisfied, would be the fifth; nay, it is as grave as the other four together."

While he yet thus spake to me jestingly, I exclaimed,

"Praised be He that recalleth all things forgot! Good mine host, knowest thou whether mine ass ate provender this night? or mayhap the wall hath fallen upon him and broken his neck, for I detect no sound of him, neither hear I his braying."

But Enan said, "Surely it is only because that he is oversated." Then said I in my heart, "Would that his speech were true, that the ass at least might be satisfied, seeing that his master was not!" He called to the slave and asked of him, "Hast given the ass his provender this night? Wherefore is his braying not heard?" The slave replied, "Good master, I did set before him both straw and provender, yea, a crib full, and he did eat and was surfeited until that his soul despised it. Would that the master's paunch were but as the paunch of the ass!" quoth he, "then would we yet be eating that which he did leave remaining." I thought in my heart, the loathly slave speaks true, but I said, "Sir, because of thy love and thy graciousness I did account all the food as manna, and, as thy table testifieth, I followed the injunction (Exodus 16:19): 'Let no man leave of it until morning.' "

But he cried upon me, saying, "Thy words are but lies and deceitfulness! How long wilt mock me and despise the sense of my discourse? Remain thou mute and be silent, then wilt thou not be abashed or ashamed. Thou hast swept my table with the besom of the destroyer; and all the food in my house that is delicious thou lustest to eat." But I said, "Good sir, remove thou thine anger from upon me and incline not thy heart to words of jest and mockery."

But he said, "And how may I remove mine anger, seeing thou hast devoured the fruit of all my labor and hast well nigh crushed me in the mill of thy jaws; then sayest thou but jest and art pleasant."

Then did I protest, "But, good sir, so hath mine eating been from mine earliest youth; ever did my heart grieve for any food that was left remaining. For my father hath trained me from earliest youth and my mother hath taught me, to the end that I deal generously with my belly and satisfy it." But he laughed a laugh that was like unto a cry, and gruffly did make answer: "Accurst be any son that doth learn so shameful a trade of his father! Who," said he, "was thy father?" "My father of blessed memory," I replied, "was a righteous and pure man, a wise physician, understanding in all things." "From thy words," said he, "I perceive thou indeed speakest true, saying that he was wise and understanding in all things; and the proof of his great wisdom is that he hath taught thee the knowledge of eating."

As we were yet speaking the lamp which was before us became extinguished, and thick darkness blinded our eyes. Enan called to his slave and said, "Speedily light the lamp!" but there was no sound or response, for wine had laid him low. I asked, "What hath become of the servant?" "Perhaps he lieth sodden," he replied, and made me sit in darkness until that the light of dawn did show itself forth through the latticework.

Then said I to Enan, "Good sir, lo, day hath broken, arouse the slave, and let him knead, and put in the dough a bit of leaven." But he said, "The flesh is yet between thy teeth, and yet thus quickly again dost desire to fill thy belly? Surely thou hast heard the saying of Hippocrates, 'Introducing new food while the old is yet in the stomach doth cause death and bereavement.'" "Truly hast thou spoken," said I, "and right is with thee in all thou hast said. But that which I have eaten hath become digested in my bowels and is destroyed, as the fire devoureth the stubble and as the flame consumeth the chaff." Said he, "The Lord plague the secretion of thy stomach, that thou be not able to restrain thy dung." But I said, "I know thou hast devised evil against me, yet hast thou not specified sufficiently in thy petition. If I be seized in respect to secretion, perhaps it would be for me salutary and healing, and the Ineffable would turn thy curse into a blessing. For Galen hath said, 'If a secretion befall a man of those humors which nature requireth to issue forth and to discharge, then do all the members seize upon it and it becometh the occasion of their well-being.'" Said he, "Though I have erred in my prayer, the Lord knoweth my meaning." "I know," said I, "the meaning of thy heart and its intent; yet the curse causeless shall not come."

Then went I for to see mine ass, and I came to the crib, but found it empty of straw and provender; nor could he complain of his sad estate; nay, I found him nigh strangled, for in such wise had the base slave muzzled his mouth that he bray not. Then came I nigh unto him to remove the muzzle, but when I had removed it he bit me, and came nigh to trampling me underneath his hoofs. So I took my cane and did belabor him until that his cries ascended the very heavens. Then did the Lord open the ass's mouth, and he said, indignant and wroth, "Wherefore smitest thou me, seeing that I be of the race of Balaam's ass?"

I was amazed at his speech and affrighted at his wrath, and thought, "Perhaps Satan speaketh from the ass's gullet"; but to the ass I said, "Wherefore should I not smite thee, seeing thou hast bitten me and nigh trampled me underneath thy hoofs?" Then said the ass, "Thyself thou satest down with that shameful man to thy pleasures and thy food, whereas I, being muzzled, watched through the night in hunger and thirst and great want." But I replied, "Am I a Balaam that understandeth sorcery? Whence should I know thou wert in hunger and in thirst, seeing that the base slave did declare unto me that thou hadst eaten sumptuously and wert satisfied, that thou hadst reclined and wert lying at ease in the corncrib?"

Then did I cry out upon the slave saying: "Wherefore wert thou about to slay mine ass with hunger and thirst, and why didst thou afflict him thus exceeding cruel?" But the slave made answer and swore that he had put straw and provender before the beast, which had then eaten and become satisfied; but that the belly of the ass was like as that of his master, for that he left nothing remaining.

"But," said I, "if thou hast indeed given him provender in sufficiency, wherefore didst thou muzzle him that I should not hear his braying?" He replied, "Because that he is an ass of evil habits, and is turbulent and doth cry out all the night. Further I was in fear lest he bite me with his tusks." "True is the saying," said I, "like slave like master. And the Arab hath said, 'The slave is but a crumb of his master's clay.' "

His master Enan overheard these remarks, and forged his tongue against me, and spake, "Wherefore dost thou set a snare for me by thy words and why hast thou reviled me, these three times?" But I answered him, "Is it for this that thou has brought me out of my city, that thou mightest slay me and mine ass with hunger?"

"Accursed be that day," said he, "whereon I brought thee out; let it not come into the reckoning of months! For I have brought thee to mine house only as a reproach and a disgrace unto myself, and as a punishment for my transgression and my guilt. Yet as my soul liveth and the soul of my grandfather Asmodeus, I will make thee cry 'Hold!' to thy folly, and I will take thee with my little finger and cut thee off and cause thee to perish utterly."

Then I looked upon him, and lo! his countenance was flames of fire and his eyes flashing sparks; and smoke issued from his nostrils as from a furnace. I inquired in a gentle voice, my soul being in great confusion, "My lord, let me but ask of thee and be not wroth, which Asmodeus was thy grandfather?" "The great prince Asmodeus," he replied, "who did lift King Solomon from his kingdom upon his pinion, and carried him afar from his country."

Then said I, "Woe betide my soul! I considered thee a dear friend and now I discover thee one of the demons, who do ensnare the spirits of mortals. Is this thy kindness to thy comrade? Wherefore didst not tell me thy race, wherefore didst thus deceive me, and bring me forth from my native country?" Said he, "And where was thine understanding and thy discernment, thy knowledge and thy wisdom? Did I not tell thee my name was 'Enan Hanatas, son of Ornan Hadesh?' Turn it about and thou wilt find it Enan the Satan, son of Ornan the demon*; son of Deathcourt, son of Mightydeath, son of

* The inversion is obvious in the original.

Deathshade, son of Dread, son of Confusion, son of Terror, son of Bereftment, son of Malady, son of Pestilence, son of Destruction, son of Minish, son of Evilname, son of Alvan, son of Javan, son of Scorn, son of Mishap, son of Plague, son of Brazen, son of Haughty, son of Sheram, son of Guilt, son of Deceiver, son of Stenchdom, son of Perish, son of Crooked, son of Curse, son of Abdai, son of Asmodeus, king of the demons, unto whom they were all servants."

When I heard all these names howling desolation seized upon me, dread and terror fell upon me; my heart forgat all joy and gladsomeness, and tremors seized my flesh. And I cried, "Woe is me for my destruction, for here will my grave be. Truly have the sages said, 'A man's feet are pledged to bring him where fate would have him.' "

But he said unto me, "Fear not nor be dismayed, and let thy speech be calm, for, as live all the souls I have mentioned, I will not forsake thee until that I have accomplished that which I spake. Arise and walk in the land, in the length of it and in the breadth of it, and behold its beauty and its goodliness; nevertheless the people be strong that dwell in the land."

Chapter XII

Zabara sojourneth in the city of Enan for a space of time. He considereth the folk thereof and findeth them wicked and sinful. The daughter of a certain wicked man of that town had found favor in the eyes of Enan and he was become enamored of her. Zabara reproveth Enan, setting forth that it beseemed him ill to wed the daughter of an unlettered man. Enan hearkeneth to Zabara's voice and taketh to wife another maiden, that was a learned man's daughter. In the course of their discussion of women and their qualities, Enan relateth the story of a certain washerwoman who caused dire commotion in the city and warfare so dread that 220 men were slain.

Then did Enan lead me through the streets and through the market places and he showed me the wizards and the sorcerers; I looked upon the city and behold, it was a place of sin and guilt, yea the sons of Anak also were there. "What may these be?" said I to Enan; "mine eye hath never beheld their like."

"They are the sons of Anak," said he, "around whose necks folly is forged as a chain. They are great and tall, yea mountainous, like as unicorns. Desirest thou," said he, "that I show thee the man I love, my boon companion, my pride and glory, for he is of my family?" "Prithee," said I, "show me him for verily I would behold his figure." So he showed me a man, like as himself in form and appearance, of a height with himself, being tall and a fool, sinful and causing others to sin. His face was the face of an ox; his beard lay upon his belly, which was as a heap of wheat, compounded with filth and dung.

Then said I, "Who is this man, whose like I shall not behold in all the city?" Said he, "He is related and a kinsman; from my youth hath he been my choice, and I have loved him. He is a great man, of good repute, yet is his wrath the wrath of a violent man, and his lineage known to all, for that he is of the seed of one hanged." "Wherefore, then, hast thou loved him," said I, "for his understanding or for his upstanding?"

"Look not on his countenance," quoth Enan, "nor on the height of his stature, but rather upon the goodliness of his traits and the greatness of his wisdom, for he is a wise man and understandeth all the sciences; his like hath not lived before him, nor will live after his death. He possesseth traits goodly and choice, far beyond those of most men."

Said I, "Tell me of his traits, and thereafter will I ask thee concerning his wisdom." Then said he, "These are his goodly traits and desirable qualities: He hateth every wise man and loveth every fool; no drink or food suffice him, nor doth he pray each day, until he have eaten. Furthermore, with a handful of onions or garlic or leeks or radishes he doth devour five loaves, having mercy upon no man. He is generous with his substance, his bread and his water — may the Lord so be with him."

Said I, "I have heard sufficiently regarding his food; but tell me, pray, wherein his generosity lieth." He replied: "He is generous of both purse and person. Every one that doth recline at his table receiveth a cloth that is torn and a napkin shredded. Once there came to his house a man hard-pressed and needy: ever did my kinsman abominate the poor and the needy. He received him with lips of kindness, and displayed his generosity before him: he gave him a little of a dry crust to eat, wherein was neither peace nor love. And in order to sour his heart, he gave him vinegar to drink that he might thirst. When the poor man refused to drink it he drave him forth from his house and took his garment, until that he paid for his fare. The poor man wept and called upon the Most High until that he drenched his garb with his tears and his habit with the blood of his liver. Then went he forth smitten and oppressed. Eager for to curse him, and in wrath and sore vexation he cried out to the people these verses:

O villainous knave, base and vile!
My coat he took from my back;
Upon him may Ebal's curse recoil,
Pursue him to ruin and wrack.

May his cup's tongue cleave to its palate in thirst,
His table's lips faint with hunger accurst.

"And as for the generosity of his person, nothing ever issued from his belly, but like a swine did he chew the cud of that which he had hid away in his entrails." "Truly may he be termed generous," said I, "nay, passing generous, who possesseth these qualities of which thou hast made mention. But now that I have heard of his good works, tell me of his wisdom." "Ask of whatever science thou wilt," quoth he, "wherever thou touchest his knowledge extendeth."

"What doth he know of medicine?" I asked. "He knoweth that every corpse is brought to burial, and he understandeth that the dead hath suffered from some disease or accident," he replied. "And of astronomy?" I asked. "He knoweth that it is day when the sun doth shine," he replied, "and he recognizeth night when the stars appear."

"Of reckoning?" "That one and one make two and that a hundred and a hundred are two hundred." "What knoweth he of geometry?" "He knoweth how many handbreadths his belly extendeth, and how many spans between his beard and his bottom."

"What of music?" "Of this science," he replied, "he understandeth more than of all the others; for he can distinguish between the barking of a dog and the braying of an ass, between the sound of weeping and of joyful music."

"What knoweth he of philosophy?" "That man may speak only from the gullet above, and break wind only from the gullet below." "And of the intercalation of the months, a science of which every individual and every community hath need?" "When he perceives that a woman's belly goeth before her he understandeth that she is pregnant.*

"And what doth he know of our Law, which is our wisdom and our understanding?" "He knoweth every statute and commandment," he replied; "for when he beholdeth the private

* This science was required by everyone because by it the calendar was fixed. An obvious pun makes the point of the rejoinder.

member he recognizeth whether it be circumcised or uncircumcised."

"So this is his wisdom of which thou hast spoken," said I: "accursed be the disciple, and the master who did reveal to him these mysteries. By thy life and the life of thy dear friend, reveal unto me all thy secret: how could a man whose works and wisdom are as thou hast thyself said, bind thy heart with chains of love?" "Wouldst hear the truth?" he asked. "I would indeed if thou wouldst but tell it," said I. "Thinkest thou," quoth he, "that I know not that there is in him neither knowledge nor discernment, that his speech is folly and without understanding, that he doeth the deeds of Zimri and keepeth the statutes of Omri, that no one cometh nigh him to remove his base folly from upon him? Yet do I esteem him neither for his honor nor his glory, but for the love of his daughter, who is fair as the moon and possesseth wit and understanding. Her do I desire for my portion, and beside her hath none found grace and favor before me, for she is upright in my sight."

"Wherein do her beauty and her comeliness lie?" I asked. "Lo," he spake, "I will tell thee. Her braids lie upon her cheeks raven black, her appearance is beauteous and her voice pleasant, her eyes are as doves, her cheeks as lilies, her lips as a thread of scarlet, her teeth as pearls, and her two breasts are as two pomegranates: I may not extol all her members, for my tongue sufficeth not for her praises. It is of her that the poet hath said:

As ruby red upon sapphires
Are thy lips upon thy teeth.
Thy countenance the sun is;
Thy thick braids like flashing night
Do overspread its brilliance.

Also:

When the eyes of a deer are red and blear
The poor beast's thirst they betoken.

But the eyes of my dear are red I declare
With the blood of the hearts she has broken.
Prowess by victim's gore is betrayed;
My lady's eyes attest her keen blade.

And again:

My lady fair
Doth set a snare
For the unwary feet of the stranger.
She lays them low
With one fell blow
Ere they perceive their danger.
She pierces the heart
With her eyes' deadly dart
And leaves the wound forever to smart.

"Yet beware," said I, "of the ignorant folk, for they work breach upon breach. And our masters have said, 'Ever should a man sell all that he possesseth in order that he may wed the daughter of a scholar; for if he die or be exiled he will be assured that his sons will be scholars. Let him not marry the daughter of an ignorant man, for if he die or be exiled his sons will be ignorant folk.' They have said further: 'An ignorant man may not eat of flesh, for Scripture saith, "This is the law of cattle and fowl"; he that occupieth himself with the Law may eat of the flesh of cattle and fowl, and he that occupieth himself not with the Law may not eat of the flesh of cattle and fowl.' And Rabbi Elazar hath said, 'It is permitted to cut down an ignorant man on Atonement Day, even if it fall on a Sabbath.' His disiciples said, 'Master, say rather to slaughter him.' He replied, 'Nay, for ritual slaughter requireth a blessing, but this requireth no blessing. Further, it is prohibited to join an ignorant man's company upon the way, for Scripture saith, It [the Law] is thy life and the length of thy days: an ignorant man regardeth not his own life, and will therefore certainly not regard the life of his neighbor.' They said further, 'It is permitted to tear an ignorant man apart as he were a fish, and one added, even down the back.' Another sage said, 'If we did not require them to carry on our business we would slay them.' Further have our sages of blessed memory said, 'If one engage in study before an ignorant man it is as if he should violate his betrothed before him, for Scripture saith, "Moses hath commanded the Law as an heritage: read not *morashah* [heritage] but *m'urasah* [betrothed]." '

"Further, greater is the hatred wherewith the ignorant hate the scholars than the hatred wherewith the nations hate Israel. Of the ignorant man, furthermore, were six things said: 'Testimony may not be committed to him, nor taken from him, secrets may not be revealed to him, he may not become a warden of the fatherless, or of charity monies, nor may his company be kept upon the road.' Some say, 'Also no public announcement may be made of articles lost by him.' They have also said, 'Calamity cometh upon the world only because of the ignorant folk, and our master Moses hath hinted in the Law that they merit stoning, for he hath said (Leviticus 20:2): 'The people of the land* shall stone him with stones': Whoso is ignorant him shall they stone.

"Further have they said, 'Ever should a man sell all that he possesseth in order that he may take to wife the daughter of a scholar; if he find not the daughter of a scholar, let him marry a daughter of the great ones of the generation; if he find not such, let him marry a daughter of the chiefs of the synagogue; if he find not such, let him marry a daughter of the wardens of charity; if he find not such, let him marry the daughter of a teacher of children.' But let him by no means marry the daughter of an ignorant man, for that they are loathly and their women an abomination, and of their daughters hath it been said (Deuteronomy 27:21): 'Cursed be he that lieth with any manner of beast.' Also have our sages of blessed memory said, 'He that giveth his daughter in marriage to an ignorant man, it is as if he bound her and cast her before a lion; for just as the lion doth tear and devour and hath no

* This expression is equivalent in rabbinic parlance to *ignorant folk* and I have so rendered it elsewhere in this passage.

shame, so doth an ignorant man strike his wife and come in to her and have no shame.' Further, when his inclination seizeth him he is as a lion that beholdeth its prey, and when his lust prevaileth over him, his wife may not restrain him. Yea, and all men who know not the five sorts of blood which the sages have pronounced unclean, and cannot distinguish between a woman that doth menstruate and one that hath a discharge, and are not careful regarding their wives' couch, their sons will not be legitimate.

"They that understand the healing art have said, 'If one lie with his wife during her period, and she conceive of that seed, the offspring will ever be leprous. If it be the first day of her period it will be leprous in its childhood; if the second day, in its youth; if the third in its prime; and thereafter in old age.' The reason is that the menstrual blood, being warmer than the remaining blood of the body, for that it is the refuse of the blood and of evil humors, is mingled with the seed whence the fetus is formed, whose nature therefore becometh as the nature of that blood; and at the periods mentioned the blood doth rot and become rancid, whence leprosy ariseth — the Lord preserve us from this disease and deliver every wise and understanding soul. As the ancient proverb hath it, 'Take not a wife for wealth or beauty, for wealth and beauty depart, and only slander abideth.' "

"Now do I know," said he unto me, "that thou hast fear of the Lord, and that thou dost cherish love of me in thine inmost heart; it is a stake fixed in a place secure. Thou hast admonished me to beware of the perils of the season; thou hast banished desire from my heart and purged naughtiness from within me; thou art of those faithful friends of whom the ancient wise men spake. For they asked of Plato, 'What is a lover?' 'When one saith, "Thou art he; thou and none beside thee," ' he replied. When Galen was asked, 'What is love?' he replied, 'Similarity of soul'; and it is the wont of similars to be conjoined, for that they are of a single nature. Another sage was asked, 'What is love?' 'Brotherly nighness of soul,' he replied, 'and not brotherly nighness of body.' They asked of Aristotle, 'What is love?' 'One heart,' said he, 'divided into two bodies.'

"Yet I do beseech thee, if I have found favor in thine eyes, seek me out another. Her that I have mentioned I shall never at all wed, for I fear lest she be an accursed plague in my house, and lest, if I have offspring of her, they resemble their grandfather; for the sage hath said, 'Even as sons resemble their fathers in members and appearance, so do they resemble their grandfathers in nature and character.' "

Said I to him, "I will give thee a maiden comely and modest, possessed of wit and understanding, yet doth she eat three and four times during the day and is never satisfied. Her father is a son of the Law, attired in righteousness as in armor; he rendereth judgment and maketh the dark to be light, but is at present in adversity."

"Meseemeth the maiden is of thy kin," he replied, "for I perceive that her paunch is as thy paunch. Yet as thou art my neighbor and my goodly comrade, I do beseech and implore thee that she be not an evil woman and hard, that she put not upon me with her voice. For the sages have said, 'An evil woman is a constant affliction unto her husband and dread of women doth search out even the hiddenmost entrails'; as befell me with a certain washerwoman." "And what was this story?" I asked. He replied:

"Once on a time I came to a certain country which dwelt safe and secure. All the day I wandered abroad in its streets and sought to become a stumblingblock for the folk, but could not; so I said, 'This is not a seat for my pleasure: I will return to mine own place and mine own country.' And it came to pass when I was departed from the city and had sat me upon the bank of a river that lo! a woman came to wash clothes, and she gazed upon me and said, 'Art thou of the sons of men or of the demons?' 'With the sons of men have I been raised,' said I, 'but my birth is of the sons of demons.' 'Whence comest and whither goest?' she asked. Said I, 'I have dwelt in this city a full month, and I have found all its inhabitants friendly and neighborly, jesting and disporting themselves one with the other; and I availed not to pour forth a spirit of mischief in their midst.' Then spake she with lips of pride and scorn, 'As thy soul liveth, because of thee do I revile all demons, for ye seem strong and mighty but are in truth weaker than women. Sit thee here and keep the clothes, and mind thou be not of the faithless. I will return thither and kindle fire and wrath among them and arouse an evil spirit upon them; then wilt thou see what will befall in the city.' Said I, 'I await thy coming, and I shall see how thy words fall out.'

"So she returned to the city and came into the house of one of the great men of the place. She addressed the mistress of the house, saying, 'Give me thy clothing and the clothing of my lord thy husband, and I will wash them as thy soul desireth.' Even as the maidservant was gathering the clothing together, the woman lifted her eyes to the lady and gazed upon the beauty of her countenance, and said, 'Cursed be all men, for they are all adulterers, a company of faithless, neither true nor loving to their wives.'

"Said the lady, 'Wherefore sayst thou this thing?' Quoth she, 'As I departed from my house but now, I saw thy husband come forth from the house of a certain harlot, and my vision was nigh distraught, for I wondered how he could forsake thy beauty, which hath praise and repute, for the sake of a harlot of loathly mien.'

"When the lady had heard these things her countenance fell and her eyes ran tears. 'Wherefore,' asked the woman, 'hath thy face fallen and thine eyes become darkened? Becalm thee, and let not thy tears fall, for I will work a matter for thee and thy love, to the end that thy husband never at all love any woman beside thee. I will remove thy reproach from upon thee, if thou but do that which I bid thee. When thy husband is returned home, after that he hath eaten and drunk, do thou beguile him, making thy words tender and thy speech smooth; cause him to fall asleep upon thy knees, and when he is fallen asleep do thou take a whetted razor and cut from his beard three hairs, be they black or white. Give them to me when I return to thee, and I will make of them a remedy that his eyes darken in their sockets from gazing any more after other women, beautiful and comely. His love will cleave to thee, that thou become great and famous, and will never be withholden from thee.'

"The lady replied, 'I will do as thou sayst, and would that love return, as thou hast spoken!'

"Then the woman took the soiled clothing and departed and went to the lady's husband, simulating vexation and faintness. 'My lord,' said she, 'there is a secret matter I would declare to thee, but I know not whether I may avail to speak of it with my tongue, for thy maidservant is sore confused from that which I have seen and heard in thy house: the Lord give my death for thine and let me not behold thy day of evil!'

"The man trembled and said to her, 'Quickly relate what thou hast heard and seen in my house, and remove the dread from upon me.'

"So she spake, 'I came to thy house, and the lady thy wife gave me these clothes to wash, and as I was yet standing there I beheld a youth handsomely clothed in a comely mantle, himself being of goodly appearance. He went with her into the chamber and they closed the door after them. As they took counsel together I inclined mine ear to hearken to their speech, and I overheard him say unto her, after that he had grasped the skirt of her habit and turned its hem backward: "Go slay thy husband, whose spirit is hard upon thee, and I will take thee to wife." Then said she to him, "And how may I slay him? I am in dread of him, and cannot do this base thing." But he said, "Cause him to sleep on thy bosom, and when his sleep is sweet upon him take thou a whetted razor and slaughter him. Make thy heart firm, lest thy hands grow faint; then will I come to thee and lodge between thy two breasts."'

"When the man heard the words of the infamous woman,

he was fair seized of an evil spirit, and dread and trembling fell upon him. He lifted his feet and strode in wrath and came to his house and spake to his wretched wife: 'Dress me my meat that I may eat from thy hand, and thereafter will I slumber a little upon thy knees.' So he did eat and drink and lay him upon her knees, but she knew not that her ways were suspect. When she perceived that he had closed his eyes, she drew forth her razor for to cut off the hair of his beard, but he speedily arose and took the razor from her hand and butchered her. Then did the lady's brethren and kinsmen assemble to the house and smite the man and slay him, and the two families became desolated, for there fell 220 of the nobles slain.

"Then did the woman return and relate all the evil she had wrought, and in all the city arose a great cry, the like of which had never been heard. So I sware upon that day that I would never harm any man more, but would form guest friendship and peace with all.

"Furthermore do I fear lest my second wife resemble her that I wed in my youth, who abided with me many years, and whom I did thereafter send away, for that I was grown weary of enduring her evil and faint from bearing the yoke of her wickedness. She was a continual dropping, and I was in dread of her voice. Upon her beauty of form and comeliness of stature, her wit and prudence, I pronounced these verses:

Demon's face on woman's brow graven,
  Her beauty doth render me a fearful craven.
Her tongue doth make my fleshly hair to stand,
  Her voice doth sever my heart sinew's strand.
She banisheth peace and maketh rife
  Dissension and quarrel and continual strife;
Her bower on contention's mount she maketh,
  This quarrelsome haunt she never forsaketh.
With the sea strand's weight she oppresseth my liver,
  Like a boiling pot she maketh mine entrails quiver.

But I said unto him, "Fear not, for I will give thee none but a maiden goodly and fair and seemly." So I gave him a certain one of the daughters of my good friend and neighbor, and he took the maiden to wife, and came nigh to her and brought her unto his house, and loved her. And when I saw that he was at peace with her and secure, I said, "Birds of a feather do flock together."

Chapter XIII

Zabara doth despise the men of that place, and desireth to return to his own land, to visit R. Sheshet Benveniste, in whose honor he did compose this book.

And it came to pass when my days in that place had grown long, that I said to Enan, "Good sir, mayst thou spend thy days in prosperity and thy years in pleasures, and behold true life with the wife thou lovest, the pleasant roe thou didst desire! Lo, I have prolonged my stay in this city and am surfeited with the sight of monstrous and vile figures and with hearing brazen words of contention. They employ, as I perceive, neither phylacteries nor *mezuzot*; nor indeed any manner of song or versification, saying that all such things are vile, that the chant of a hen or goose is to be preferred. Their wisdom is comprised in discerning whether cattle be fat or lean. Upon the right hand the youths arise in violence and on the left churls are exalted. The young deal frowardly with the old, and the lightly esteemed with those full of honor; men of prudent heart are subject to fools.

"Yet for all this had we remained silent and had hardened our eyes to the desecration of things hallowed, but for the reproach of the Law of our Lord, which is the light of our eyes, our pride and our glory, our hidden treasure, which hath been reviled by reason of our iniquities. Just as the wise man taketh pride in his wisdom and the mighty man in his strength, so do some of them take pride in lies and cunning deceitfulness, and some in their light-headedness and some in their slander and some in their brazenness and licentiousness.

"And all this brutish folk is smitten of the plague of slander, which kindleth the fire of hatred and arouseth the breath of envy; nor do these children of wickedness understand that slander is the worst of all sins and transgressions. Our sages

— their memory abide for a blessing — have said, 'Slander slayeth three: him who telleth it; him who receiveth it; and him of whom it is told.' They have said further: 'Slander is worse than idolatry and adultery and murder.'* Of idolatry it is written (Exodus 32:31): 'Oh, this people have sinned a great sin, and have made them gods of gold'; of murder it is written (Genesis 4:13): 'And Cain said unto the Lord, my punishment is greater than I can bear'; of adultery it is written (Genesis 39:9): '[And Joseph said to the wife of Potiphar], how then can I do this great wickedness, and sin against God?' But of slander is it written (Psalms 12:3): 'The Lord shall cut off all flattering lips and the tongue that speaketh proud things.'

"But these people spread false reports abroad, and do hate without cause. They render others tainted with their own taints and faults, everyone that dwelleth in the midst of their uncleanness.

"To all this are they brought by their frowardness and their brazenness, as is found in the sayings of the sages: Judah the Prince saith, 'The froward are doomed to Gehenna, and the meek to Paradise.' Of a brazenfaced person R. Eliezer saith, 'He is a bastard'; R. Joshua saith, 'He was conceived during menstruation'; R. Akiba saith, 'He is a bastard conceived during menstruation'; R. Judah saith, 'His forbears stood not at Sinai's foot.' And the Arab hath said, 'Better a meek bastard than a legitimate son that is brazen.' Furthermore, the Chaldaeans have said in their proverbs, 'The brazen pursue after adultery.'

"If one of their elders or their great or prudent men arise to rebuke them and to chide them for all their wickedness and sinfulness and transgression, and bespeaketh them softly in language choice and clear, saying, 'Do not, my brethren, work wickedness, and neglect not prudence and instruction, and guard ye from excommunication, for he doth not live upon whom it falleth' — then do they mock scornfully and say:

* These three are the cardinal sins, to avoid which martyrdom was prescribed.

'There shall be no excommunication in Israel. We are bound to regard neither oaths nor things devoted, nor have we care of aught save field and vineyard.' Better in their sight than masters of science and men of kindness and faith are they that sanctify themselves and purify themselves in the gardens (Isaiah 66:17). They arise early and watch late to set up posts wherein to make contention and strife to glow. Their speech is falsehood and they are masters of deceitfulness; their faces glow ruddy, but they are slack in the work of the Lord. Among them are sufferers of gonorrhea, and leprosy, and epilepsy; of them hath the poet sung:

Among this folk thou wilt see
One who riseth betimes and speedily
  To God's House wendeth his way.

"He doth offer his heart, humble and contrite
For that he hath sinned in his Maker's sight,"
  Perceiving, thus wilt thou say.

But in his heart is naught of prayer,
For quarrel and strife goeth he there,
  To dispute and not to pray.

And again:

Would you call a place House of Praise
  If folly there doth abide?
If a man be ignorant of paths and ways,
  Would you call such a one guide?
Then why do you call it House of Prayer,
When epileptic lepers foregather there?

And also:

How feel secure? How trust mankind
When friends deceive and neighbors blind,
Making the right to seem the left,
Nor guile disdaining nor patent theft;
Their thoughts on prey and violence fell,
With no hope of Heaven, no fear of Hell?
Only in secret crypt may I abide hidden
As a heretic book of the sages forbidden.

And yet again:

My heart doth burn, my soul repine
For the comrades dear I must needs resign;
Unfriended, alone to abide constrained,
Of kin bereft, by sad loneliness pained.
How may I dwell mid folk boorish and sot
Who draw descent from the seed of Lot,
Whose forebears lorded some Philistine village,
Their pride to thieve, their science to pillage?

"To me it seemeth also that all are of equal degree, for that princes dwell with the meek and fools with the prudent. But though their congregation comprise wise and understanding men, who dispense righteousness and keep faith, yet do the froward among them prevail — not in number or rank, nor in wealth or substance, forasmuch as the good are greater in number and in wisdom and in other respects — but in frowardness and guile and deception; among these are the Levites not numbered, for there are indeed those who understand how to do godly service in the sanctuary of the Law and in the assembly.

"Therefore do I let my supplication fall before thee, if I have but found favor in thine eyes, grant my petition, fulfill my request, bring me forth hence and cause me to return to mine own place, that I may spend my latter days in peace with my kinsmen and my neighbors. Most eager am I to return to my country and my birthplace, to take sweet counsel with my peers and the men of my family; full many years now have I dwelt a stranger in a foreign land, with soul sorrowful and bitter. I cannot dwell in a city where only fools and boors receive honor: in that city do I desire to reside where the hoary sage hath his seat."

Said Enan, "And who is the hoary sage of whom thou speakest, ascribing to him high merit?" "A man in whom is the spirit of God," said I, "and who possesseth God-like understanding. He is the choice one of the generation and the pride of the age. He is liberal and deviseth liberal things and by liberal things doth he stand. He is a man of wisdom and discernment, a master of kindness and faith, great in works and good deeds. To tell all his praises, to enumerate all his qualities, were wearisome; he is a prince and a noble in Israel, dealing with the holy nation in faith and governing the people of God. He is esteemed as is the merit of his soul — the great prince Rabana Sheshet ben Benveniste, may his memory be for a blessing and a pride so long as the city's gates turn upon their hinges. Him doth wisdom call bosom friend and companion; faith, beloved and neighbor; governance calleth him redeemer and comrade; generosity doth call him gentle one and delight; loving kindness calleth him fellow and peer; and righteousness, intimate and associate."

Then said Enan unto me, "What are his great works which have brought him all these virtues?" Said I, "Perfection and Humility and Uprightness and Holiness. Our masters have interpreted (Deuteronomy 23:9): 'Keep thee from every wicked thing: Let a man not indulge in impure meditations by day, that he may not descend to uncleanliness by night.' Hence saith Phineas ben Jair: 'Strictness resulteth in scrupulousness; scrupulousness resulteth in cleanliness; cleanliness resulteth in abstinence; abstinence resulteth in purity; purity resulteth in being hallowed; being hallowed resulteth in fear of sin; fear of sin resulteth in meekness; meekness resulteth in holiness; and holiness is the greatest of all, as Scripture declareth (Psalms 89:19): "Then *Thou* spakest in vision to Thy holy one." '

"Herein is Phineas in disagreement with Joshua ben Levi, who saith: 'Meekness is the greatest of all, as Scripture showeth (Isaiah 61:1): "The Spirit of the Lord God is upon me; because the Lord hath annointed me to preach good tidings unto the meek"; Scripture saith not the *holy* but the *meek*; hence we learn that meekness is the greatest of all.'

"The version of the passage in the Palestinian Talmud is as follows: 'Scrupulousness resulteth in cleanliness, as Scripture saith (Leviticus 16:19): "Hallow from uncleanliness." Cleanliness resulteth in purity, as Scripture showeth (Leviticus 14:20): "And the priest shall make an atonement for him and he shall be pure." Purity resulteth in being hallowed, as it is written (Leviticus 16:19): "And cleanse it and hallow it." Being hallowed resulteth in meekness, as Scripture indicateth (Isaiah 57:15): "For thus saith the high and lofty One that inhabiteth eternity, whose name is Holy; I dwell in the high and holy place, with him also that is of a contrite and humble spirit, to revive the spirit of the humble, and to revive the heart of the contrite ones." Meekness resulteth in fear of sin, as it is written (Proverbs 22:4): "By humility (and), fear of the Lord." ' Isaac ben Elazar saith: 'That fear of the Lord which Wisdom maketh the crown of her head, Humility maketh the imprint of her shoe, as Scripture saith (Psalms 111:10): "The fear of the Lord is the beginning of wisdom"; yet elsewhere is it written (Proverbs 22:4): "By [homonym for *foot-print of*] humility (and), fear of the Lord." Fear of the Lord resulteth in a hallowed spirit, as it is said (Proverbs 2:5): "Then shalt thou understand the fear of the Lord, and find the knowledge of God." A hallowed spirit resulteth in holiness, as Scripture saith (Psalms 89:19): "Then *Thou* spakest in vision to Thy holy one." Holiness resulteth in resurrection of the dead, as it is written (Ezekiel 37:13-14): "When I have brought you up out of your graves, and shall put my spirit in you, and ye shall live." And resurrection will result in the coming of blessed Elijah, as the prophet saith (Malachi 4:5, 6): "Behold I will send you Elijah the prophet before the coming of the great and dreadful day of the Lord; and he shall turn the heart of the fathers to the children, and the heart of the children to their fathers, lest I come and smite the earth with a curse." '

"May the Almighty find him worthy to be numbered with the righteous, and may mine own soul die the death of the upright, and may He, in the abundance of His loving kindness, place my lot with His servants. Amen."

* * * * *

	Explicit	*Liber*	*Zabarae*	
Domino	*gloria*	*mundi*	*totius*	*Creatori*

THE SEATS OF THE SOUL

THE SEATS OF THE SOUL

Joseph, the son of Meir, the son of Zabara, may his memory be for a blessing, saith:

The opening of my speech and the beginning of my discourse is the praise of Him who maketh me to sing, who hath neither inception nor beginning, neither end nor completion, who doth generate matter out of naught, who is everywhere found though His place is unknown.

And at the head of His creations, to consummate His deeds, He created four foundations, in whose composition are miracles and mysteries: each of them is unlike his fellow in name, and virtue, and effect, and nature.

Corresponding to these He created in the body of man four humors, each of which possesses two virtues. He doubled, that is, the nature of the four heads; the primary virtues are active, and the others are acted upon.

He created man in wisdom, dust out of the earth, and He endued his form with breath, and rendered him excellent in speech, and appearance, and erectness, and He bound into his being the rational soul, and therein does man surpass the beasts.

And He endued man's body with three spirits, which should lead and conduct him: The one in the brain, which is the soul spirit which causes motions, at times wearying him and at times rousing him; thence are the five senses which constitute the life of the soul.

The second is in the heart. This is the vital spirit which causes man to live, and renders him discerning in all his deeds and wise in all his ways.

The third is in the liver. It is the natural spirit which sustains man, and whensoever his food is wanting it nurses him with blood, which it differentiates in its essence and nature in respect to all his members. The virtue of this natural spirit occurs in all creatures and in all species of trees and herbs.

Further did He vouchsafe loving-kindness unto man in that He created in him compartments and perforations. Some conduct the breath in their midst, and some gather their needs from the aliment; and some cleanse man's being, by reason of the aliment and its stench.

Therefore doth it behoove every man to bless and to praise Him for all the good He hath conferred upon man; to exalt Him, to honor Him, to sanctify Him, and to declare His unity, in the thoughts of his heart and in his imaginings, when he sitteth, and when he riseth, and upon all his ways, for that He hath satisfied all his needs. And I His servant, the son of His handmaid — ever will I declare His unity, and by my songs will I glorify Him; may the Name of His glory be praised and exalted, forever and eternally. Amen and amen.

* * * * *

These Are the Seats of the Soul, a Delight and a Refreshment to All Who Read Them:

To the First whose beginning is without beginning
And whose end is without end or completion,
Be reverent, O my brother; to Him attend with all thy Heart,
Ever shall He enter upon thy thoughts;
Both at eventide and in the morning, prayer
Shalt thou order before Him: to Him meet is praise.
Sustain thy heart with His love and His majesty,
And cleave to the memory of His glorious Name.
Seek of Him, humble thyself before Him,
Beseech Him as a slave his master.
With all thy heart seek and search for Him,
That He may guard thy feet from a snare and a stumbling.

* The following poem of 126 metrically-correct, rimed couplets bears Zabara's full name in acrostic. The translation is literal and line for line, with no attempt at meter.

Keep His law and His commandments and His statutes,
And hew to the line for all the judgments of His utterance.
Exalted is He above all blessing,
And His dread is guarded and prepared.

For He hath wrapped the ends of the orbit in wisdom;
And man knoweth not whyfore and wherefore
He hath created him, and made his content clay,
And established him upon naught with breath.
Firmaments He spread upraised in this orbit and placed
Lights therein, and the sun, which is as a bridegroom.
In wisdom did His hand establish the foundations,
And miracles, four, and their secrets
Are set each opposite the other in their virtues,
In cold and heat and dryness and moisture.
He recalled them to fashion of them creatures,
And placed man at the head of those created.
He made him excellent in majesty, appearance, erectness,
In a soul that knoweth wisdom and cunning.
Truth He placed in his mouth, to Himself to utter
And Him to praise for all His deeds.

Behold that which He hath put into man's head,
To seek out the true from the false and the good from the evil.
Truly three powers hath He put therein [the brain],
And in three chambers do they abide therein;
Imagination, ratiocination, and recollection are they,
And by them man excels the beasts in majesty.
And He did put discretion into the heart of man,
And He will grant slumber to his eyelids.

To man's eyes He gave the power of vision,
Whereby he sees all that is before him,
Through two passages which are hollow;
None in the body but these are perforated,
For the others are created solid all,
That they be the firmer and stronger.

Likewise hearing did He bestow upon man's ears,
Whenever sound shall come into its hidden chambers.

Also with his nostrils to smell every scent,
And to feel all that he touches with his hands.
Yet further have pleasant lots befallen
The tongue, the taste of nine sorts;
Which are: Bitter, and sweet, and the insipid,
Which is the lowliest and humblest of tastes;
Sour, salt, and nutgall;
The sharp taste which separates and spreads;
And must, and fat: lo, these
Tastes were created nine after their kind.

He hath ordained in man the extension of motor veins
To his members, at his pleasure at all times;
He puts them into motion at his will
For his need, according to his strength and vigor.
Of these [members] two are without will,
And they draw the breath for life.
These are the lungs, which are ever inflated,
And the heart, which draws their content in abundance.

Teeth did He set into man's mouth, mighty ones;
And these are divided into three classes:
Grinders He ordained to crush and make fine;
To them He joined dog teeth, to break and to tear;
And some are incisors, planted
For the [pronunciation of] the middle letters.
Of roots the lower teeth have two;
For the upper three are counted.
Into the mortar of the jaw are these builded,
And this is their strength, for they are but suspended.

He ordained that there be a windpipe,
That breath might ever pass in its midst.
A curtain He placed at the mouth of the windpipe to close it
When man swallows, lest he perish if food passed down.

A gullet He provided back of the windpipe,
Whereby all food and drink might pass.
The lungs at its end He fixed,
Hidden in the chamber of the ribs,
Arranged to breathe upon the heart —
And may its breathing not be slight —
So that the heart in its heat might not
Consume the remainder of the body and its bread.
Therefore is an animal ritually unfit if its lung be perforated,
For then its wound hath no healing.

The stomach is bound to the end of the gullet
With sinews to hold it fixed;
A vessel it is to receive the food
Whereby the soul of its master liveth.
To it hath He given power to draw the food,
And secondly to retain the food hath He ordained it;
The third power is to grind it,
The fourth to expel it.
In six hours is food digested there,
And after six it is cleansed away and thrust out.

An entrail hath He placed at its mouth as a doorkeeper;
It watcheth ever the going out of the food,
And at other times it is closed; it awakens
To open its mouth at the time of the going out and gapes open.
Ever is it ready for the stomach even as a slave,
Whereby to issue forth its food to the liver.
Of every man is the length of its end
As twelve times the measure of his finger.

This one is appointed to empty it forth into yet another
Which is perpendicular, so that the food be not delayed.
And the second delivers it unto his fellow;
There the natural force retains it.
This entrail alone is diagonal

Unto the liver which is placed at its side,
So that the food might not by a perpendicular path
Issue forth, and depart too speedily.

Thence to the liver, which is set as a guard
To suck out, without a mouth, that which has been kept;
The essence of the food it draws and makes drip,
Even as that marvelous stone draws iron.
There in six hours is it rendered red,
And with its heat seethes until it becomes blood.
The liver purifies (and separates the blood) into three humors:
— The red bile, lest by its heat it burn man
He sent into a hidden sac,
And set it a margin, as a sword in a sheathe;
For its strength is as fire, hot and dry —
And He heals with the three, and He preserves.

To the spleen He sends the black bile,
So that it be not spread abroad in the blood;
For it is dry and cool,
And its nature is as the earth which was accursed.
The third humor is like unto spittle;
Its nature is as water, moist and cool.
Balgam is it called in the Arab tongue.
It is situate in the head and the breast and the lungs,
And does not dwell alone as do the others,
Which are very evil and cool.
Thereafter He sendeth the blood into the body —
Its nature is warm, like breath, and also moist —
Through the veins, which at their source
Are filled with blood to sustain the body:
Therein is man's life, that is his strength and might.
In every portion it is converted into its kind:
In bone it is rendered into bone, also in flesh
To flesh it turns, that naught be consumed or wanting.

To the kidneys He sends the remainder,
Of blood are they taken and numbered.
And He presses it until it is like unto blood
Within water; but it is red.
Thereafter He sends it to the bladder,
Which is ever the known source of the urine,
Through two passages that are wide,
Which the Arabs call *brabich*.
There is it twice purified,
And cleansed until it is rendered as water;
Water indeed it is, but called urine.
By means of it physicians discern diseases,
Because it is the remainder of the blood and its essence,
And for many diseases it is man's agent.
Its fluidity and condition and nature
Testify to the disease of the body and its nature.

The Creator of the bladder wrought miracles in its evacuations,
For therein is water contained,
And it is within the body, open for water,
Which ascends, in its going forth, with wind.
There is yet another marvel in its devising,
For when it is full it is restrained from issuing forth.
Therefore should a man grasp the hem of his garments,
And before all uncover his feet.

The remnant of the food goes into the intestines,
And is there ever rendered into excrement.
The red bile hastens it,
And forces the intestines to expel it.
The entrail which is underneath He ordained
To thrust it forth and cleanse the body.
And thereby also do they discern
The disease of the body, and therefrom do they judge,
By its digestion, and also by its color and odor
Do they discern, when they observe and smell it.

Of entrails in the body six are known,
All fixed for the need of the aliment.
The situation of the liver He placed on the right side
Of the stomach, that it be as a fire to the pot;
And on the left side the spleen, to cool
The heat of the heart, for there heat nesteth.

He hath made a prison house for the private parts
Whereby men are ensnared
To beget thereby, to be conjoined with women;
Thence do man children arise.
That blood the lust of a man draws
And gathers from all his members.
By their heat is it seethed until it becomes
As milk, somewhat thick in its issuing forth.
And inasmuch as *all* the members are its source,
Man is therefore created in his own image and likeness.

The heart of man He created in two chambers,
To discern therewith and to understand mysteries.
He set its order in the ribs of the left side,
That it might not stand between the boundaries.
In one [chamber] reside man's life and spirit,
And the other is filled with blood in its strength;
This is the best of the liver's blood, its pride,
And thereby are the heart and brain nourished;
It increases strength and resorbs it.
Thence is favor and anger,
And thereby is man's spirit soft or hard;
For in it are both strength and weakness,
And from it are sorrow and joy
And brazenness and humility and meekness;
Thereby does man's inclination rouse him to every desire.
Therefore should a man repress his inclination,
Nor believe that in [following] it is his peace;
For if he sin herein he will perish by his sin.

God hath made the heart master over all the members;
The throbbing veins are its agents,
For they are ordered from its source,
And are watchful over man's every deed.
Therefore the physicians, when of his two arms
The veins they feel, understand all a man's nature
Thereby; for by a straight line are they drawn [from the heart],
And of flesh and hair are they bare.
They understand the matters of the body and its function,
Its every disease and pain and hurt.
Their wisdom is according as its disease;
In their healing they understand its lack,
And they do for it according to its rule and statute,
Until its Master restore it to its strength —

With the aid of the Rock who wounds and heals,
By whose Name the invalid and diseased are strengthened,
Who was before all, and will ever be;
He causeth to die, and thereafter quickeneth the dead.
He is the Lord who setteth all into motion,
He maketh men wise, and wise men He maketh fools.
What shall man who withereth like grass say,
Except that he beseech the face of his Creator and pray
That He deal with His servants daily
According to the measure of His mercies and abundant loving-kindnesses.

May it be His will to forgive
The iniquity of His servant, as His mercy telleth,
And sprinkle upon his sins the waters of forgiveness
To quench the fire of sorrow and sighing,
And may He turn His fountains to the panting soul,
And break its thirst with His pleasant waters.
With the souls of those who trembled at His word
Bound up may it be in His precious bond;
Before Him may it enwrap itself in garments of comfort,

And find rest after death.
As for His people who declare the unity of His glorious Name
And daily testify His greatness and majesty —
As of old may He bear them as a nurse
In the bosom of His love. Amen; amen.

Consummatum laus Deo.

EPISTLE DEDICATORY

DEDICATORY DISCOURSE TO RABANA SHESHET BEN BENVENISTE *

Here is my book; with clearness writ,
Hewn from lofty peaks of wit,
Of sayings of the wise compounded,
And the speech of those in knowledge grounded;
Golden words, in crucible tried
Lest baser dross therein abide;
By reason's rod I render measured
What for long my heart hath treasured.

To Sheshet I send it, my people's lord
Beloved of all, esteemed, adored;
To him alone myself I yield
Of all who rule or power wield.
My body is his, my head, my heart;
With all, for him, I gladly part,
A cheerful slave, in bondage free,
Nor redemption awaiting, nor jubilee.

And would my heart to my breast return
Its fickle faithfulness I should spurn.
My spirit too, in like degree
Awaits his pleasure and would not be free.
If to strangers my love it confessed
My very heart I'd tear from its breast.

* This dedicatory poem occurs, naturally, at the head of the book. Its matter however, is irrelevant to the body of the book, except in so far as it throws light upon the life of the author. Its merit being no better (and, it should be added, no worse) than most productions of its kind, it has been thought best to consult the interest of the reader and relegate it to its present position. The version reproduces the original line for line. As in the original the lines are of unequal length.

Except my tears the mystery revealed
  From the envious all my secret I'd shield.

For my neck a chain, a garland for my brow
  His name doth weave, his fame bestow.
With steel his love in my heart is limned
  By time uncorroded, by years undimmed.

His discourse sweet doth my palate sooth,
  Of manna its flavor, gentle and smooth.
Into my being's fiber his Book I conjoined
  Lest envious charge, Thou hast it purloined.
More delicious far than honey's drip
  Its fragrant counsel doth caress my lip.
'Gainst need it furnisheth my warrior gear,
  Corselet and shield and balanced spear.

Slumber mine only solace is, for then I seem
  To behold my lost lord, though in shadowy dream.
Yea, and my cup also doth ever pledge his memory,
  But my wine runs tears for him I long to see.
Vexation and sorrow's blood my face have stained,
  Tears gush to lave it, but were they not restrained
By the heat of my gall, then would they flood
  All my spare frame, bereft of blood.

My kindled wrath doth my spleen distort,
  For that with a fool I must needs consort;
'Tis a burden sore upon my shoulders
  As were Tabor's mount piled on Nophel's boulders.
Came his person within my grasp savagely I'd burn it,
  Sounded his name as doth mine own quickly I'd unlearn it
Save as a term of abuse and insult, reproach and contumely,
  Though sweet to me erst it were and passing seemly.
If but his filthy touch besmirch my habit
  With potent lye and naphtha straightway would I lave it.
Were not my soul's honor his life's defense
  Which restraineth mine ire with prudent sense,

Swordless would I slay him with my lung's mighty breath;
As a butcher a ram, so would I compass his death.

As lion ravening a lamb devoureth, tearing limb from limb,
So with whetted tongue unsheathed would I dismember him.
Seemly shame restraineth me from naming my base foe;
It suiteth ill my dignity to contend with one so low.

Hated and contemned am I of folly's numerous horde,
For them have I despised; I cleave to wisdom's frugal board.
In wisdom's comely robes I clothe me passing fair,
Garb of prudence with faith begirt about my person I bear.
On wisdom's strait and chastened path joyfully have I trod,
My bread I break, my rest I take on prudence' grateful sod.
With prudent feet have I won their folly's flood across
Thyself, said they, didst turbid made it; if thou leave thine own's the loss.

Mastering my lower nature, my sordid lusts have I represt,
Banishing base inclination, purging evil from my breast.
From utterance vile and discourse unseemly is my mouth by virtue ruled,
To pearls of wisdom and gems of wit industriously schooled;
Open wide to friendship's word and speech of gentle peace
But against violence bolted fast and guarded without surcease.

Hath a friend against me sinned, mine honor wounded deep,
I yield mine honor's dignity, no grudge have I to keep.
Never did pauper needy from my door-step depart aggrieved,
Ever I fed the hungry, with my wealth their want relieved;
The sick, as far as in me lay, I eased of every ill,
Freely bestowing of my substance, generously giving of my skill.
And if aught of these my claims of merit be proven but boasting vain

Then defeat I freely confess; exult, mine enemies, your foe is slain!

Grant to thy bard, noble lord, his humble supplication;
Accept for thy fame's sweet sake his hymn of dedication.
Whatever of wisdom herein lies, whatever of hidden lore,
Thine the merit for aught of worth; my learning is of thy store.
My reason blunt did I whet that it
Might perceive the brilliance of thy wit.

And since its erudition all from learned Sheshet I took
'Tis but just I grave his name upon the title of my Book.
Raiment of song have I featly spun, bravely to deck my lord,
Broidered praises for his name have I woven, as best my skill doth afford;
Like jewels on a necklace his praises I arrayed, that they beseem his favor,
Like myrrh and nard and frankincense, and aloe's pungent savor.

But more I give beyond perfume, and jewels and comely attire —
My heart I offer with my book: accept it, gracious sire.
Thy glorious title adorn my book, that the effulgence of thy fame
May some slight reflected splendor shed upon my humble name.

Also for Sheshet:

Receive Shaashuim — Book of Delight,
Composed in thy name, Master:
Solace in exile, refuge in flight
Mind's comfort in disaster.

And again:

Who hath graven upon parchment
Words of limpid fire,

Gladsome tidings, sweetly uttered?
  If one should inquire,
"Faithful Joseph, friend beloved,"
  So answer, gentle sire.

And also:

My heart with sorrow is afflicted sore
  Whelmed by floods of tears.
Take these songs: would they restore
  My joy and banish my fears!

BIBLIOGRAPHY

BIBLIOGRAPHY

WORKS MARKED * HAVE NOT BEEN AVAILABLE FOR CONSULTATION.

Abrahams, I., The Book of Delight and Other Papers, Philadelphia, 1912.

Abrahams, I., "Joseph Zabara and his 'Book of Delight,'" *The Jewish Quarterly Review*, VI (1893-94), pp. 502-32. Reprinted in the preceding work.

Abrahams, Israel, A Short History of Jewish Literature from the Fall of the Temple . . . to the Era of the Emancipation, London, 1906.

*Adelard of Bath, Quaestiones naturales perdifficiles. Questions 33 and 51 printed in Davidson (*q.v.*), Sepher Shaashuim, Appendix C.

Adolphus, *see* Fabulae Adolphi.

Æsop, Fables of, *see* Jacobs; L'Estrange; Townsend.

Albertus Magnus, *see* Borgnet.

Al-Hariri, *see* Chenery.

Amador de los Rios, José, Estudios históricos, politicos y literarios sobre los Judíos de España, Madrid, 1848.

Apocrypha, The, "The Story of Tobit."

Aristotle, Meteorologica, *see* Ideler.

Aucassin et Nicolette, *see* Suchier.

Barbazan, Étienne, (ed.), Fabliaux et contes des poètes françois des xi, xii, xiii, xiv et xve siècles, tirés des meilleurs auteurs; publiés par Barbazan. Nouvelle édition, augmentée et revue sur les manuscrits di la Bibliothèque Impériale, par M. Méon, Paris, 1808. 4 vols.

Bebel, August, Die mohammedanisch-arabische Kulturperiode, Stuttgart, 1889, 2. Auflage.

Bédier, Joseph, Les Fabliaux, Paris, 1925, 4. éd. rev. et corr.

*Benfey, Theodor, "Die kluge Dirne," Kleinere Schriften von Theodor Benfey, ausgewählt und herausgegeben von Adalbert Bezzenberger . . . Gedruckt mit Unterstützung Sr. Excellenz des königl. preussischen Herrn Cultusminister und der königlichen Gesellschaft der Wissenschaften zu Göttingen (Berlin, 1890-92, 2 vols.), Bd. I, 1e und 2e Abteilung.

—— (tr.), Pantschatantra, Leipzig, 1859.

Benjamin of Tudela, *see* Grünhut und Adler.

Bergen, Henry, (ed.), Lydgate's Fall of Princes (The Carnegie Institution of Washington), Washington, 1923-27, 4 vols.

Blau, Ludwig, "Raphael," Jewish Encyclopedia, X (1905), 317-19.

Boccaccio, Giovanni, Il decamerone.

Boethius, Anicius Manlius Severinus, De consolatione philosophiae.

Boinet, É., . . . Les Doctrines médicales, leur évolution, Paris, [1905].

Bolte, Johannes, und Georg Polivka, Anmerkungen zu den Kinder- und Hausmärchen der Brüder Grimm, Leipzig, 1913-30. 4 vols.

Borgnet, Augustus, (ed.), B. Alberti Magni . . . opera omnia, Vol. XI (De animalibus), Parisiis, MDCCCXCI.

Bozon, Nicole, *see* Smith et Meyer.

Breen, A. E., "Asmodeus," Catholic Encyclopedia, I, 792.

Broydé, Isaac, "Translations," Jewish Encyclopedia, XII, (1906), 219-29.

Bulaeus, *see* Du Boulay.

Castoiement d'un père a son fils, Le, edited by Barbazan (*q. v.*), II, 39-183.

Catholic Encyclopedia, The, New York, 1907-12, 15 vols.

Cento novelle antiche, Le, *see* Sicardi.

Chenery, Thomas, (tr.), The Assemblies of Al-Hariri, Vol. I [no more published], London, 1867-98.

Choulant, Johann Ludwig, (ed.), Aegidii Corboliensis carmina medica, Lipsiae, 1826.

Christ, Wilhelm von, Geschichte der griechischen Literatur, München, 1920, 6. Auflage.

Clouston, W. A., Popular Tales and Fictions, Edinburgh and London, 1887, 2 vols.

Compilatio singularis exemplorum, *see* Hilka.

Conde Lucanor, El, *see* Knust.

Conybeare, F. C., "The Testament of Solomon," *Jewish Quarterly Review*, XI (1899), 1-45.

Crane, Thomas Frederick (ed.), The Exempla . . . of Jacques de Vitry (Publications of the Folk-Lore Society, XXVI), London, 1890.

Daremberg, Ch., Histoire des sciences médicales, Paris, 1870, 2 vols.
Davidson, Israel, (ed.), Sepher Shaashuim . . . by Joseph ben Meïr ibn Zabara (Texts and Studies of the Jewish Theological Seminary of America, IV), New York, 1914.
Delitzsch, Franz, Zur Geschichte der jüdischen Poesie vom Abschluss der heiligen Schriften alten Bundes bis an die neueste Zeit, Leipzig, 1836.
Diepgen, Paul, Geschichte der Medizin, II (Mittelalter), Berlin and Leipzig, 1914 (Sammlung Göschen, no. 745).
Diogenes Laertius, *see* Hicks.
Dozy, R., Recherches sur l'histoire et la littérature de l'Espagne pendant le moyen âge, Paris and Leyden, 1881, 3e éd. rev. et augm., 2 vols.
Drach, (ed.), Sainte Bible de Vence, Paris, 1827-33, 5e éd., 27 vols. and 1 vol. app.
Driscoll, James F., "Raphael," Catholic Encyclopedia, XII, 640.
Drum, Walter, "Tobias," pt. II, Catholic Encyclopedia, XIV, 750-53.
*Du Boulay, César Égasse, Historia universitatis Parisiensis, Parisiis, 1665-73, 6 vols.
Dukes, Leopold, Philosophisches aus dem zehnten Jahrhundert, Nakel and Leipzig, printed 1868.
Dunlop, John, History of Prose Fiction, *see* Liebrecht.
Ellis, Geo., (ed.), Specimens of Early English Metrical Romances, London, 1811, 2d ed., 3 vols.
Encyclopædia Britannica, The, Cambridge, England, 1910-11, 11th ed., 29 vols.
Encyclopædia Judaica, Berlin, 1928- .
Ersch, J. S., und J. G. Gruber, (editors). Allgemeine Encyclopädie der Wissenschaften und Künste, Leipzig, 1818-50, 167 vols.
Étienne de Bourbon, *see* Lecoy de la Marche.
Fabliaux, *see* Barbazan; Montaiglon et Raynand.
Fabulae Adolphi, edited by: (1) Polycarp Leyser (*q. v.*), Sect. XIV, no. VIII, pp. 2007-36; (2) Thomas Wright (*q. v.*), Latin Stories, Appendix II, pp. 174-91.
Foerster, Richardus, (ed.), Scriptores physiognomici Graeci et Latini, Lipsiae, 1893, 2 vols.
Frazer, Sir James George, Folk-Lore in the Old Testament, London, 1919, 3 vols.

Friedländer, Moses, (tr.), The Guide for the Perplexed, by Moses Maimonides, New York, 1910, 2d ed., rev. throughout.

Gabirol, *see* Zangwill.

Garrison, Fielding H., An Introduction to the History of Medicine, Philadelphia and New York, 1929, 4th ed., rev. and enlarged.

Gaster, Moses, (tr.), "Two Unknown Hebrew Versions of Tobit," *Proceedings of the Society for Biblical Archaeology*, XVIII (1896), 208-22, 259-71; XIX (1897), 27-38.

Gerard of Cremona, (tr.), Abubecri Rasis ad regem Mansorem de re medicina, Liber II translatus ex Arabico in Latinum. Section on physiognomy edited by Foerster (*q. v.*), II, 161-79.

Gesta Romanorum, *see* Oesterley, Hermann.

Gilles de Corbeil, *see* Choulant.

Ginzberg, Louis, "Asmodeus," Jewish Encyclopedia, II (1902), 217-20.

Gollancz, (Hermann), (tr.), Tophet and Eden (Hell and Paradise), in Imitation of Dante's "Inferno" and "Paradiso," from the Hebrew of Immanuel ben Solomon Romi, London, 1921.

Gower, John, *see* Morley.

Graetz, Heinrich Hirsch, Geschichte der Juden von den ältesten Zeiten bis auf die Gegenwart, Leipzig, 1897-1911, 11 vols.

Grimm, Die Brüder, *see* Kinder- und Hausmärchen.

*Grisebach, Eduard, Die Wanderung der Novelle von der treulosen Witwe durch die Weltliteratur, Berlin, 1886.

Grünhut, L., und M. N. Adler, (translators), Benjamin ben Jonah von Tudela, Reisebeschreibungen, Frankfurt a. M., 1903-4, 2 vols.

Gubernatis, Angelo, Comte de, La Mythologie des plantes, New York, 1872, 2 vols.

Gueulette, [Thomas Simon], Les Mille et un quart (*sic*) d'heure, Contes tartares (Cabinet des Fées, XXI; XXII, 1-241), Genève, 1786.

Gunkel, Hermann, Das Märchen im Alten Testament, (Religionsgeschichtliche Volksbücher für die deutsche christliche Gegenwart, II. Reihe, 23.-26. Heft), Tübingen, 1917.

Gutmann, Jehoschua, "Aschmedai," Encyclopædia Judaica, III (1929), cols. 498-501.

Hadas, Moses, "Gadarenes in Pagan Literature," *The Classical Weekly*, XXV (1931), 25-30.

Hagen, Friedrich Heinrich von der, und Johann Gustav Büsching, (editors), Deutsche Gedichte des Mittelalters, 1. Bd., Berlin, 1808.

Handbuch der Geschichte der Medizin, begründet von Dr. med. Th. Puschmann. . ., bearbeitet von Professor Dr. Arndt. . ., herausgegeben von Dr. med. Max Neuburger, Vol. I, Jena, 1902.

Haskins, Charles Homer, The Renaissance of the Twelfth Century, Cambridge, Mass., 1927.

Haupt, Moritz, und Heinrich Hoffmann, (editors), Altdeutsche Blätter, Leipzig, 1836, 2 vols.

*Herolt, John, Promptuarium exemplorum. Wright (*q. v.*), Latin Stories, No. C, has edited tit. Matrimonium from this work.

Hervieux, Léopold, (ed.), Les Fabulistes latins depuis le siècle d'Auguste jusqu'à la fin du moyen âge, Paris, 1893-99, 5 vols.

Hicks, R. D., (ed. and tr.), Diogenes Laertius, Lives of Eminent Philosophers (The Loeb Classical Library), London, 1925, 2 vols.

*Hilka, Alfons, (ed.), Neue Beiträge zur Erzählungsliteratur des Mittelalters, Compilatio singularis exemplorum, Sonderabdruck aus dem 90. Jahresbericht der schlesischen Gesellschaft für vaterländische Kultur.

——— und Werner Söderhjelm, (editors), Die Disciplina clericalis des Petrus Alfonsi (Sammlung mittellateinischer Texte, I, kleine Ausgabe), Heidelberg, 1911.

Hirschfield, Hartwig, (tr.), Kitab al Khazari, by Judah Hallevi, New York, 1927, 2d ed.

Hulme, W. H., "A Middle English Addition to the Wager Cycle," *Modern Language Notes*, XXIV (1909), 218-22.

Husik, Isaac, A History of Mediæval Jewish Philosophy (Jewish Publication Society of America), New York, 1930.

Hyamson, Moses, (ed. and tr.), B^{e}hai ben Joseph ibn Bakoda . . . Duties of the Heart, New York, 1925.

Ibn Gabirol, *see* Zangwill.

Ideler, J. L., (ed. and tr.), Aristotelis meteorologicorum libri IV, Lipsiae, 1834-36, 2 vols.
Immanuel ben Solomon Romi, *see* Gollancz.
Irmischer, *see* Plochmann und Irmischer.
Jacobs, Joseph, (tr.), The Fables of Æsop, London, 1889, 2 vols.
——— "Spain," Jewish Encyclopedia, XI (1905), 484-502,
Jacques de Vitry, *see* Crane.
Jewish Encyclopedia, The, New York and London, 1901-06, 12 vols.
*John of Bromyard, Summa prædicantium. Selections published by: Wright (*q. v.*), Latin Stories, no. XXI; Wesselski (*q. v.*), Mönchslatein, no. VI.
John of Salisbury, *see* Webb.
Juan Manuel, *see* Knust.
Judah Halevi (Hallevi), *see* Hirschfield; Salaman.
Jugement de Salemon, Le, edited by Barbazan (*q. v.*), II, 440-42.
Karpeles, Gustav, Geschichte der jüdischen Literatur, Berlin, 1920-21, 3. Aufl., 2 vols.
Katten, M., "Elijahu," in part, Encyclopædia Judaica, VI (copyright, 1930), cols. 485-94.
Kayserling, Meyer, Geschichte der Juden in Spanien und Portugal, Berlin, 1861.
Keller, Adelbert von, (ed.), Hans Sachs (Bibliothek des litterarischen Vereins in Stuttgart), Tübingen, 1870-1908, 26 vols.
Kinder- und Hausmärchen gesammelt durch die Brüder Grimm, original Ausgabe, Stuttgart and Berlin, 1906, 32. Auflage besorgt von Rheinhold Steig.
Knust, Hermann, (ed.), Juan Manuel, El libro de los enxiemplos del Conde Lucanor et de Patronio, Leipzig, 1900.
Köhler, Rheinhold, Kleinere Schriften zur Märchenforschung, Vol. I, Weimar, 1898; Vols. II and III, Berlin, 1900.
Krauskopf, Joseph, The Jews and Moors in Spain, Kansas City, 1887.
Kressner, Adolf, (ed.), Rustebuef's Gedichte, Wolfenbüttel, 1885.
Kusa Jātakaya, *see* Steele.
La Fontaine, Jean de, Fables (Oeuvres complètes . . . avec

des notes . . . par M. C. A. Walckenaër, Paris, 1878, pp. 1-129).
Lancereau, Édouard, (tr.), Pañchatantra, Paris, 1871.
Landau, L., "Hebrew-German Romances and Tales and their Relation to the Romantic Literature of the Middle Ages," *Teutonia*, 21. Heft, Leipzig, 1912.
Laurie, S. S., The Rise and Early Constitution of Universities, New York and London, 1903.
Lecoy de la Marche, A., (ed), Anecdotes historiques, légendes et apologues tirés du receuil inédit d'Étienne de Bourbon (Société de l'histoire de France), Paris, 1877.
L'Estrange, Sir Roger, (tr.), Fables of Æsop and Other Eminent Mythologists: with Morals and Reflexions, London, 1694, 2d ed. corrected and amended.
Leyser, Polycarp, Historia poetarum et poematum medii ævi, Halæ Magdeb., MDCCXXI.
Liebrecht, Felix, John Dunlop's Geschichte der Prosadichtungen . . . aus dem Englischen übertragen und vielfach vermehrt und berichtigt, Berlin, 1851.
Liljeblad, Sven, Die Tobiasgeschichte und andere Märchen mit toten Helfern, Lund, 1927.
Luther, Martin, *see* Plochmann und Irmischer.
Lydgate, John, *see* Bergen.
Maimonides, *see* Friedländer.
Mangenot, E., "Démon dans la Bible et dans la théologie juive," Vacant et Mangenot (*q. v.*), IV, cols. 322-39.
Martin, Ernest, (ed.), Le Roman de Renard, Strasbourg and Paris, 1882-87, 3 vols. and suppl.
*Mensa philosophica, translated in part by Wesselski (*q. v.*), Mönchslatein, no. CLI.
Meyer, Paul, (ed.), Les Contes moralisés de Nicole Bozon, *see* Smith et Meyer.
Montaiglon, Anatole, et Gaston Raynaud, (editors), Receuil général des fabliaux, Paris, 1872-90, 6 vols.
Morley Henry, (ed.), Tales of the Seven Deadly Sins, being the Confessio amantis of John Gower, London, 1889.
Munk, Salomon, Mélanges de philosophie juive et arabe (Bibliothèque d'histoire de la philosophie), Paris, 1927.
Münz, Isak, Die jüdischen Ärtzte im Mittelalter, Frankfurt a. M., 1922.
Neckham, Alexander, *see* Wright.
Neuburger, Max, Geschichte der Medizin, Stuttgart, 1906—, Vols. 1—.

Odo of Sheriton, Fables. Edited by Hervieux (*q. v.*), IV (Eudes de Cheriton et ses dérivés).

Oesterley, Hermann, (ed.), Gesta Romanorum, Berlin, 1872.

Oesterley, W. O. E., and G. H. Box, A Short History of the Literature of Rabbinical and Mediæval Judiasm, London and New York, 1920.

Ordronaux, John, (ed. and tr.), Regimen sanitatis salernitanum, Philadelphia, 1871.

Pantchatantra, *see* Benfey, Lancereau.

Paquda, Bahya ibn, *see* Hyamson.

Paris, Gaston, "Le Cycle de la gageure," *Romania*, XXXII (1903), 481-551.

Peregrinus, edited by Leyser (*q. v.*), Sect. XV, pp. 2099-2120, no. XXVI.

Petrus Alphonsus, *see* Hilka und Söderhjelm.

Petronius Arbiter, Satyricon.

Pfeiffer, Franz, (ed.), "Predigtmärlein," *Germania*, III (1858), 407-44.

*Plath, Margarete, "Zum Buch Tobit," in *Theologische Studien und Kritiken*, LXXIV (1901), 377-414.

Plochmann, J. G., und Dr. Johann Konrad Irmischer, (editors), Dr. Martin Luther's sämmtliche Werke, Frankfurt a. M. and Erlangen, 1826-57, 67 vols.

Predigtmärlein, *see* Pfeiffer.

Puschmann und Arndt, *see* Handbuch der Geschichte der Medizin.

Rashdall, Hastings, The Universities of Europe in the Middle Ages, Oxford, 1895, 2 vols.

Rhazes, *see* Gerard of Cremona.

Regimen sanitatis salernitanum, *see* Ordronaux.

Regné, Jean, "Étude sur la condition des Juifs de Narbonne du 5. au 14. siècle," Narbonne, 1912, reprinted from the *Revue des Études Juives*, LV, 1-36, 221-43; LVIII, 75-105, 200-25; LIX, 59-89; LXI, 228-54; LXII, 1-27, 248-66; LXIII, 75-99.

Roman de Renard, *see* Martin.

Rutebeuf, Li Diz de l'erberie, edited by Kressner (*q. v.*), pp. 115-20.

Sachs, Hans, Ein fasznacht-spil mit vier personen: der Teuffel mit dem alten weib. Edited by Keller (*q. v.*) in the Bibliothek des litterarischen Vereins in Stuttgart, CXXV (1875), 35-46.

*Sachs, Michael, Die religiöse Poesie der Juden in Spanien, zum 2. Male herausgegeben von S. Bernfeld, Berlin, 1901.

Sainte Bible de Vence, *see* Drach.

Salaman, Nina, (tr.), Selected Poems of Judah Halevi, Philadelphia, 1924.

Salomon und Morolf, edited by von der Hagen und Büsching (*q. v.*), I (last selection), 55-56.

Schmidt, Hans, "Jona, eine Untersuchung zur vergleichenden Religionsgeschichte," *Forschungen zur Religion und Literatur des Alten und Neuen Testaments*, IX, Göttingen, 1907.

*Scot, Michael, De physiognomia et de hominis procreatione. *C.* 1200. Several early printed editions.

Secretum secretorum. Section on physiognomy edited by Foerster (*q. v.*), II, Sect. V c, pp. 181-222.

Seven Wise Masters, The, edited by Ellis (*q. v.*), III, 71-78.

Shakespeare, William, King John.

Sicardi, Enrico, (ed.), Le cento novelle antiche (Bibliotheca Romanica, nos. 71, 72, Biblioteca Italiana), Strasburgo, n. d.

Simrock Karl, Der gute Gerhard und die dankbaren Todten, Bonn, 1856.

Singer, Charles Joseph, A Short History of Medicine, New York, 1928.

Smith Lucy Toulmin et Paul Meyer, (editors), Les Contes moralisés de Nicole Bozon, Paris, 1889.

Speculum laicorum, *see* Welter.

*Steele, Thomas, Alagiyavanna Mohoṭṭāla. An Eastern Love-story. Kusa Jātakaya, a Buddhistic Legend, London and Edinburgh, 1871.

Steinschneider, Moritz, "Zabara," Ersch und Gruber (*q. v.*), II, Vol. XXXI, pp. 93-96.

——— Hebraeische Uebersetzungen des Mittelalters und die Juden als Dolmetscher, Berlin, 1893.

Stock, St. George, "Tobit, The Book of," Encyclopædia Britannica, XXVI, 1041-42, 11th ed.

Suchier, Hermann, (ed.), Aucassin et Nicolette, Paderborn, 1921, 9. Auflage, bearbeitet von Walther Suchier.

Sulzbach, A., "Die poetische Litteratur [of the Jews] vom

siebenten bis zum siebzehnten Jahrhundert," Winter und Wünsche (*q. v*), III, 1-215.
——— "Joseph ben Meïr Ibn Sabara," Winter und Wünsche (*q. v.*), III, 140-50.
Testament of Solomon, The, *see* Conybeare.
*Thoms, W. J., (ed.), Fabularum anecdotorumque collectio ad usum prædicantium in seriem alphabeticum digesta.
Tobit, The Story of, *see* Apocrypha; Gaster.
Townsend, G. F., (tr.), Æsop's Fables, London, [19-?].
Vacant, A., "Ange," Vacant et Mangenot (*q. v.*), I, cols. 1189-1271.
——— et E. Mangenot, (editors), Dictionnaire de théologie catholique, Paris, 1909 — .
Van den Gheyn, J., "Asmodée," Vigouroux (*q.v.*), I (1895), cols. 1103-04.
Vigouroux, F., Dictionnaire de la Bible, Paris, 1895-1912, 5 vols.
Webb, Clemens C. I., (ed.), John of Salisbury, Polycraticus sive De nugis curialium, Oxonii, MCMIX, 2 vols.
Welter, J. -Th., L'Exemplum dans la littérature religieuse et didactique du moyen âge, Paris, 1927.
——— (ed.), Speculum laicorum, Paris, 1914.
Wesselski, Albert, (tr.), Märchen des Mittelalters, Berlin, 1925.
——— (tr.), Mönchslatein, Erzählungen aus geistlichen Schriften des XIII. Jahrhunderts, Leipzig, 1909.
Winter, J., und August Wünsche, (editors), Die jüdische Litteratur seit Abschluss des Kanons, Trier, 1894-96, 3 vols.
Wise, Stephen S., "Ibn Gabirol, Solomon ben Judah. . . ," Jewish Encyclopedia, VI (1904), 526-32.
Wright, Thomas, (ed.), Alexander Neckam, De naturis rerum, de laudibus divinae sapientiae (Rolls Series), London, 1863.
——— (ed.), A Selection of Latin Stories from Manuscripts of the Thirteenth and Fourteenth Centuries, (Percy Society: Early English Poetry, Ballads, and Popular Literature of the Middle Ages, VIII), London, 1842.
Zabara, *see* Davidson.
Zangwill, Israel, (tr.), Selected Religious Poems of Solomon ibn Gabirol . . . (Schiff Library of Jewish Classics), Philadelphia, 1923.

INDEX

INDEX

DROPSIE COLLEGE LIBRARY